SOILS AND OTHER GROWTH MEDIA

SOILS AND OTHER GROWTH MEDIA

A.W. Flegmann, Ph.D.
Raymond A. T. George, BSc, NDH, MIBiol.

Lecturers in the School of
Biological Sciences,
University of Bath

AVI PUBLISHING COMPANY, INC.
Westport, Connecticut

AMERICAN EDITION
1977
THE AVI PUBLISHING COMPANY, INC.
Westport, Connecticut

© *Copyright 1975; A. W. Flegmann
and Raymond A. T. George*

Library of Congress Cataloging in Publication Data

Flegmann, A   W
  Soils and other growth media.

  Includes index.
   1. Soil science. 2. Artificial plant growing
media. I. George, Raymond A. T., joint author.
II. Title.
S591.F59 1977   631.4   77-12215
ISBN 0-87055-240-6

Printed in Great Britain

CONTENTS

PREFACE

It is well established that plants can be raised to maturity without the assistance of soils, yet most plants are (and will be for the foreseeable future) grown on soils or similar growth media. A good understanding of the basic physical and chemical principles underlying the soil processes that contribute to plant growth facilitates the intelligent use of the soil, one of our major natural resources.

This book has been written primarily for students of horticulture and agriculture in universities and colleges, who are embarking on their first and probably only course in soil science. It presents the modern views on the chemical and physical aspects of soils as the environment of plant roots on a molecular scale, together with an up-to-date evaluation of field soils and currently used growth media. The biological and biochemical aspects of soil science are not considered here in detail because of lack of space.

The book is in two parts. Part I, Basic Principles, starts with a discussion of the microstructure of soil materials, concentrating on the components of the finely divided (or clay) fraction, and continues with a description of the structure and properties of the microcrystalline clay minerals, the amorphous inorganic and organic soil materials and clay-organic complexes. This is followed by a discussion of the pore space, which contains soil water and soil air, and constitutes the molecular environment of roots. Soil water is in contact with and is replenished from the soil solid phase, and contains in ionic form the nutrients required by plants. The next chapter is a discussion of the ionic components in the environment of plant roots. Part II, Horticultural Principles, opens with a discussion of the macroscopic structure and composition of soils and other growth media. The management of soils is then discussed from the physical, chemical and biological points of view.

A book of limited size covering a wide field is necessarily selective; moreover, such selection is bound to be subjective to a certain extent. Attention has been concentrated on fundamental principles; these are presented critically where it was thought desirable. The authors have drawn on a large body of knowledge accumulated by many workers in the soil sciences whom it is impossible to acknowledge individually; most of those to whom the authors are indebted appear in the bibliography, where key references are listed together with suggestions for further reading. We are grateful to the Editor of the series, Professor L. Broadbent, for his interest and encouragement, and to our wives who have helped with the preparation of the manuscript.

A. W. Flegmann
Raymond A. T. George

PART I

BASIC PRINCIPLES

CHAPTER 1

MICROSTRUCTURE OF SOIL MATERIALS

It is a matter of common observation that all growth media are heterogeneous, consisting of solid, liquid and gaseous phases. A heterogeneous system is said to be disperse when its constituent phases are thoroughly intermixed. One of the phases of disperse systems is usually continuous in the sense that it is possible to move from any point to any other point within that phase without leaving it; in the remaining phases this is not possible. In growth media, *water* can be regarded as the continuous phase and the discontinuous phases are the *soil solids* and the *soil air*. This may at first seem paradoxical, but soil particles are always covered by thin water films even when air dry. Particles of soil solids are therefore never in direct contact. In a field soil the particles are nevertheless close enough to form loose networks and are prevented from free, unrestricted motion; such systems are known as gels. When mixed with a larger amount of water, the soil-water system is referred to as a *suspension*.

In an aqueous suspension of any natural soil and in suspensions of most other growth media, the size of the dispersed particles varies from the molecular to the macroscopic; such suspensions are said to be *polydisperse*. Soil particles can be classified according to size in many ways; two such classification schemes in common use are presented in table 1.1. The size of the particles in a soil suspension varies without

Table 1.1

Particle size limits for soil fractions

International Society of Soil Science Scheme		US Department of Agriculture Scheme	
Fraction	E.S.D.† range (mm)	Fraction	E.S.D. range (mm)
Coarse sand	2.0 − 0.2	Very coarse sand	2.0 − 1.0
Fine sand	0.2 − 0.02	Coarse sand	1.0 − 0.5
Silt	0.02− 0.002	Medium sand	0.5 − 0.25
Clay	<0.002	Fine sand	0.25− 0.10
		Very fine sand	0.10− 0.05
		Silt	0.05− 0.002
		Clay	<0.002

† Equivalent spherical diameter.

discontinuity; any classification based on particle size must therefore be largely arbitrary. A useful distinction can nevertheless be made between soil particles that may be brought into a colloidal state of dispersion and those which cannot be so dispersed. A *colloidal dispersion* is one in which the dispersed phase consists of small particles with mean diameters of less than about 2 micrometres. Both classification schemes shown in table 1.1 refer to the particles with mean diameter of less than 2 micrometres as the *clay fraction*; the rest of the soil is classified into different *silt* and *sand* *fractions*.

The particle size fractions of the soil solid phase are themselves not homogeneous, but consist of a variety of inorganic and organic materials. Two aspects of the structure of soil solids are the microstructure, or the structure of the crystalline and amorphous soil materials on a molecular scale, and the structure of whole soils or soil aggregates on a macroscopic scale. The microstructure of soil materials will be discussed first.

1.1   THE ROLES OF SOIL PARTICLE SURFACES AND OF THE SOIL PORE SPACE

Both the clay and the non-clay fraction influence the properties of soils as plant growth media, but their individual roles are rather different. This difference can best be appreciated by considering the surface area and pore volume relationships in systems of considerably simpler geometry than that of real growth media. A set of uniform spheres is a convenient model for this purpose.

The importance of the clay fraction derives mainly from the large contribution of this material to the surface area of the soil particles. Considering the effect of the radius of spherical particles on their specific surface area, as shown in table 1.2, the surface area of a given weight of spherical particles varies inversely with the particle radius. Whereas the assignment of spherical shape to soil particles is only a rough

Table 1.2

Radii and surface areas of spherical particles

Particle radius (mm)	Specific surface area† (m² /g)
1	0.00115
0.1	0.0115
0.01	0.115
0.001	1.15
0.0001	11.5

† A particle density of 2.6 is assumed, which is characteristic of most inorganic soil materials.

approximation, table 1.2 shows that most of the surface area of soils is associated with the clay fraction.

Although plant roots are thought to obtain most of their nutrients, other than CO_2, from the soil solution, this solution is usually very dilute with respect to all nutrients and therefore needs constant replenishment from the soil solids, particularly from the surfaces of these solids. Moreover, the soil solution, at least in soils of moderate moisture content, is located in the vicinity of the surfaces of soil particles (figure 1.1). Most

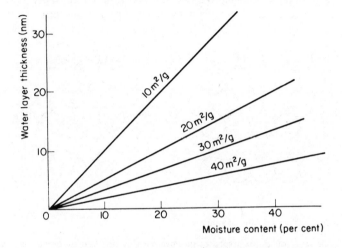

Figure 1.1 Average thickness of water layers at soil particle surfaces.
The figure shows the influence of the specific surface area of soils on the thickness of water layers at soil particle surfaces at various soil moisture contents by weight per cent $(1 \text{ nm} = 10^{-9} \text{ m})$.

of the common nutrients in the soil solution are known to enter plant roots as ions; the retention of ions by the surfaces of colloidal particles depends mainly on the presence and distribution of electric charges on these surfaces. In addition to affecting the ability to retain ions, electric charges on colloidal soil particles also affect the attractive and repulsive forces between the particles themselves: these forces determine, though in no simple fashion, the macroscopic physical properties of the soil. It is therefore clear that the microstructure of materials making up the colloidal fraction of soils will need consideration in some detail.

It would, however, be wrong to assume that the soil particles or aggregates larger than colloidal size are unnecessary and that an ideal growth medium could be formulated without them. Indeed, the opposite is true: a good growth medium need not necessarily contain particles of colloidal size. What is required is a material with a large specific surface area and moderate affinity for the retention of ions and of water. In productive soils these are most commonly realized by the presence of a colloidal fraction; but porous materials which cannot be colloidally dispersed may also provide extensive internal surfaces. Examples of potentially good growth media of this type are some peat-based composts and ion exchange resins.

The role of coarse particles, or of aggregates of fine ones, in a productive growth medium is indirect but essential; it is connected with the pore volume or, more appropriately, with the pore-size distribution. This can best be understood by considering a set of spheres in close packing (figure 1.2). In assemblies of close-packed uniform spheres the

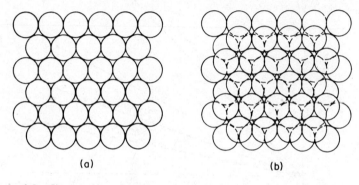

(a)   (b)

Figure 1.2   Close packing of spheres

(a) Single layer of uniform spheres in close packing; (b) two superimposed layers of close-packed spheres.

percentage pore volume is constant (about 26 per cent) and is independent of the radius of the particles. A given pore volume can therefore be realized by close packing of uniform spheres of any size.

In a growth medium, however, the distribution of pore sizes is at least as important as is the total percentage pore volume. The reason for this becomes apparent from Poiseuille's relation, according to which the rate of flow of liquid through a capillary is proportional to the fourth power of the pore radius. To maintain reasonable flow rates for infiltration and drainage in a porous medium, at least part of the pore volume must consist of large pores. The model of a straight capillary of uniform cross-section is, of course, not directly applicable to growth media in which the size and geometry of the pores is very variable. If, however, the pore space in a porous medium with irregular pore size distribution is regarded as a network of more or less cylindrical channels, the pore space can be characterized by a *mean hydrodynamic pore radius*, which takes the place of the capillary radius in the flow equation. This hydrodynamic pore radius is proportional to the pore volume/surface area ratio in a given volume of the porous medium. A large specific surface area therefore results in a small hydrodynamic pore radius and, conversely, large particle radii lead to large hydrodynamic pore radii and thus to faster flow rates.

It can be concluded that the importance of particles of larger than colloidal size in growth media derives primarily from their effect on the pore-size distribution; consideration of the microstructure of soil materials can therefore be confined to the colloidal fraction and to coarse grained porous media with large internal surface areas.

For the present purpose these soil materials will be divided into inorganic and organic. Crystalline clay minerals and amorphous clays are the main representatives of the inorganic group; humic acids, fulvic acids, peats and ion exchangers are examples of the organic types. Organo-mineral mixed systems will also be considered: most *natural whole soils* can be regarded as belonging to this category.

1.2 MICROCRYSTALLINE INORGANIC SOIL MATERIALS

Clay mineral structures

The clay fraction of soils, that is the fraction consisting of particles with a mean diameter of less than 2 micrometres, is heterogeneous and is neither chemically nor mineralogically well defined. Clay minerals, which represent a major component of the clay fraction, are reasonably well defined mineralogically and their chemical composition, although variable, is subject to certain restrictions.

The foundations of the modern study of clay mineral structures were laid in the early 1930s by Linus Pauling. Pauling based his considerations on the generalized observation that complex ionic crystals (that is those built of small tri- or tetravalent cations and large mono- or divalent anions) could be regarded as consisting of regular polyhedra with the centres of the polyhedra occupied by cations, the corners by anions. For instance, figure 1.3a shows the structure in plan view of cristobalite, a form of silica (SiO_2); this structure can be regarded as consisting of tetrahedra with silicon atoms at their centres and oxygen atoms at their corners. Similarly, figure 1.3c shows an octahedral layer of alumina, $Al(OH)_3$ and figure 1.3d an octahedral layer of brucite, $Mg(OH)_2$. Every octahedral centre-site in brucite is occupied by a magnesium ion, whereas in alumina only two out of three octahedral sites are occupied. In each layer the structure is continuous in both lateral directions. The dimensions of the repeat units, known as the a and b lattice parameters, are also shown in the diagrams.

The key to the elucidation of clay mineral structures was Pauling's observation that the a and b lattice parameters of cristobalite and of alumina were sufficiently similar to allow the two different layers to be superimposed geometrically. To link the two layers, it is only necessary to rotate half of the silica tetrahedra so that they all point in the same direction (figure 1.3b) and let the oxygen atoms at the appropriate corner of the silica tetrahedra be shared between a silicon atom in tetrahedral

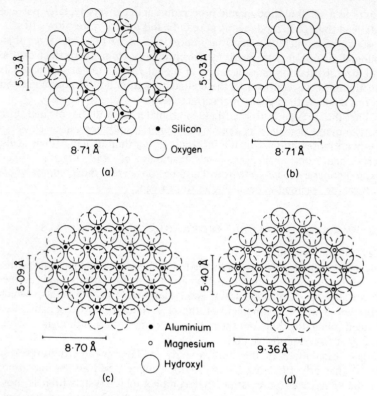

Figure 1.3   The tetrahedral and octahedral sheets in the layer silicate minerals.

(a) Tetrahedral sheet of SiO_2 from cristobalite; (b) tetrahedral sheet of SiO_2 in which all the tetrahedra point in the same direction; (c) octahedral sheet of gibbsite $Al(OH)_3$; (d) octahedral sheet of brucite $Mg(OH)_2$.

coordination and an aluminium or magnesium ion in octahedral coordination. By joining two tetrahedral layers to either side of an octahedral layer, a composite layer of about 1 nanometre thickness results. If only one tetrahedral silica layer be joined to one octahedral layer the resulting composite layer is approximately 0.7 nanometres thick. These composite layers are the units of which the layer silicates are built and they are known as unit layers of the 2:1 and 1:1 type respectively.

In addition to unit layer type a further criterion for distinguishing between the various layer silicate structures is the degree to which the octahedral centre sites are occupied. When the octahedral cations are predominantly trivalent aluminium ions, and only two-thirds of the available octahedral sites are occupied (see figure 1.3c), the structure is said to be *dioctahedral*. The perfect *trioctahedral* crystal, on the other hand, has divalent magnesium ions in octahedral positions and all the octahedral sites are occupied (see figure 1.3d).

Schematic structures of the most important clay minerals (figure 1.4) show the contents and the arrangement of atoms in the repeating unit of clay crystallites known as *unit cells*. The unit cell formulae for

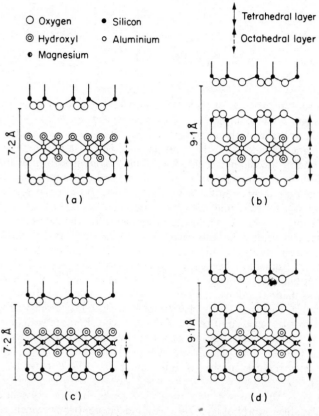

(a) (b)

(c) (d)

Figure 1.4 Schematic structure of the 2:1 and 1:1 type layer-silicate minerals

(a) Two-layer dioctahedral minerals (kaolinites); (b) three-layer dioctahedral minerals (pyrophyllites); (c) two-layer trioctahedral minerals (serpentines); (d) three-layer trioctahedral minerals (talcs).
The lattices of the montmorillonites and micas can be derived from the pyrophyllite lattice by substitution of cations of appropriate coordination.

dioctahedral and trioctahedral minerals are shown in table 1.3. These structures are electrically neutral, as can be confirmed by summing the charges on the component ions Si^{4+}, Al^{3+}, Mg^{2+}, O^{2-} and OH^-. The ions within the unit layers are held together by primary valence forces. The attractive forces between adjacent unit layers are much weaker in

Table 1.3

Unit-cell formulae for clay minerals

Subgroup	*Unit layer type*	
	2:1	1:1
Dioctahedral	$(Si_8)^{IV}(Al_4)^{VI}O_{20}(OH)_4$	$(Si_4)^{IV}(Al_4)^{VI}O_{10}(OH)_8$
Trioctahedral	$(Si_8)^{IV}(Mg_6)^{VI}O_{20}(OH)_4$	$(Si_4)^{IV}(Mg_6)^{VI}O_{10}(OH)_8$

comparison: in 1:1 type layers *hydrogen bonds* are thought to be involved, whereas for 2:1 type layers only the universal *van der Waals forces* will be operating. It is therefore not surprising that clay minerals are easily cleaved along planes parallel to the unit layers. The distance between two corresponding atomic planes in adjacent unit layers is known as the *basal spacing* of the clay mineral; these are 0.72 nm and 0.91 nm for the 1:1 and 2:1 type unit layers respectively (figure 1.4). These basal spacings are characteristic of clay mineral types: they can be altered for most clay minerals by suitable experimental treatments in the laboratory. Basal spacings can readily be estimated from X-ray diffraction patterns of suitably pretreated clay mineral samples, which can be identified in a mixture of soil clays by X-ray diffraction on this basis. The modern classification scheme for layer silicates is based on layer types and division into dioctahedral and trioctahedral subgroups (table 1.4). In addition to 2:1 and 1:1 type unit layers clay minerals with 2:1:1 type layers are also known. In these clays unit layers of the 2:1 type alternate with octahedral layers of brucite. Interstratified clay minerals are also known to occur in the clay fractions of soils. Crystallites of these minerals (also known as *mixed layer clays*) consist of unit layers of different types stacked together.

The layer structure of clay minerals suggests that the crystallites may have plate-like morphology. This was indeed confirmed when electron microscopes became available around 1940. The plate-like morphology is most pronounced for the hexagonal crystallites of kaolinites. The mean diameter/thickness ratio for the platelets varies: kaolinite crystallites usually consist of several tens of unit layers. The platelets of illite (a hydrous mica type mineral) are thinner; they normally consist of approximately ten unit layers. Montmorillonite yields very thin particles; platelets from a well-dispersed montmorillonite suspension may be only a few unit layers thick. The average thickness of 1:1 and 2:1 layer clay crystallites is indeed expected to differ in the manner just described due to the existence of interlayer hydrogen bonding in the former, and weaker van der Waals forces in the latter type of crystal.

Table 1.4

Classification scheme for the layer silicate minerals †

Type	Group	Layer charge per unit cell	Sub-group	Species ‡
1 : 1	Kaolinite – serpentine	0	Kaolinites	Kaolinite, halloysite
			Serpentines	Chrysotile, antigorite
2 : 1	Pyrophyllite – talc	0	Pyrophyllites	Pyrophyllite
			Talcs	Talc
	Smectite	0.5 – 1.0	Dioctahedral smectites	Montmorillonite, beidellite
			Trioctahedral smectites	Saponite, hectorite
	Vermiculite	1.0 – 1.5	Dioctahedral vermiculites	Dioctahedral vermiculite
			Trioctahedral vermiculites	Trioctahedral vermiculite
	Mica	2	Dioctahedral micas	Muscovite, paragonite
			Trioctahedral micas	Biotite, phlogopite
2 : 1 : 1	Chlorite	variable	Dioctahedral chlorites	
			Trioctahedral chlorites	Pennine, clinochlore

† See R. C. Mackenzie, *Clay Minerals*, **6** (1965), 124.
‡ Only a few examples given.

Some clay minerals exhibit other than plate-like morphology. For instance, crystals of the mineral attapulgite are needle shaped. The crystal structure of this clay mineral is unusual in that it is not of the layer type. The terms 'clay mineral' and 'layer silicate' are therefore not quite synonymous: the meaning of the former is both wider and narrower than that of the latter. The term 'clay minerals' includes silicate minerals which do not have a layer structure (for example attapulgite) and it also excludes some layer silicate minerals which occur as particles larger than about 2 micrometres.

The limited size of clay crystallites is probably a result of the existence of strains in the lattice. Such strains can arise from the fact that the fit between undistorted tetrahedral and octahedral layers is only approximate (see figures 1.3a and c). Other sources of strain are cation substitutions in the crystal lattice: such substitutions can occur both in the tetrahedral and in the octahedral layers and will be discussed in the next section.

Electrically charged sites on clay mineral surfaces

A valuable property of clay minerals as components of growth media is their ability to retain ions from solution and, in exchange, release ions held at their surfaces. This phenomenon, known as *ion exchange*, was originally discovered on *whole soils* in the middle of the nineteenth century. The nature of the soil materials responsible for ion exchange was controversial for a long time; it is now known that clay minerals are certainly, though not exclusively, involved. Both cations and anions are retained and exchanged by clay minerals but the cations to a much larger extent than the anions.

The question arises: how can a clay mineral with a structure as shown in figure 1.4 act as an ion exchanger? In other words, where on the crystal are the charged sites which can be neutralized by external cations or anions and exchanged by other ions from the solution?

It is now well established that the charged sites on clay minerals arise in two ways: by the cation substitutions inside the crystal structure mentioned already, and by ionization of alumina and of silica at the edges of the crystallites.

The cations shown in the pyrophyllite structure (figure 1.4b) are silicon and aluminium, while the talc structure (figure 1.4d) contains silicon and magnesium ions only. It has been shown however by careful chemical analyses of many 2:1 layer clays which have been freed as far as possible from impurities such as silica, that extensive substitution of both octahedral and tetrahedral cations exists in the clay mineral unit layers. Tetravalent silicon in tetrahedral coordination is often replaced by trivalent aluminium; this is known as *tetrahedral substitution*. The commonest octahedral substitution is divalent magnesium for trivalent

Table 1.5

Crystal ionic radii †

Ion	*Ion radius ($\mathring{A}$)*
Si^{4+}	0.42
Al^{3+}	0.51
Fe^{3+}	0.64
Mg^{2+}	0.66
Li^+	0.68
Fe^{2+}	0.74
Na^+	0.97
Ca^{2+}	0.99
K^+	1.33

† *Handbook of Chemistry and Physics.* The Chemical Rubber Co. 50th ed. 1969-70.

aluminium; magnesium may be replaced by monovalent lithium. In each case, the substituting ion has a radius not very different from the one it is replacing (table 1.5). These replacements are known as *isomorphous substitutions*. Large cations, such as sodium or calcium, are never found inside unit layers of clay minerals in isomorphous substitution. These substitutions in the clay mineral structure are believed to occur in nature during the formation of the clay, and only very slowly (if at all) once the clay mineral has been formed. The valency of the substituting cations is in most cases lower than the one being replaced. The crystal therefore carries a resultant net negative charge: this charge is neutralized by external cations.

The extent of substitution can be expressed as the layer charge per unit cell. The 2:1 layer clay minerals are listed in table 1.4 in order of increasing layer charge. The extent of isomorphous substitution increases from zero in the pyrophyllite-talc group to two charges per unit cell in the mica type minerals. In montmorillonite and in hectorite, the substitution is largely octahedral: Mg^{2+} replaces Al^{3+} in montmorillonite and Li^+ replaces Mg^{2+} in hectorite. Tetrahedral substitution occurs extensively in vermiculite and in nontronite: in both cases Al^{3+} replaces Si^{4+}. The external cations neutralizing the excess negative charge on the lattice are the exchangeable cations; the amount of exchangeable cations per unit weight of clay is the *cation exchange capacity* (CEC), normally expressed in milliequivalents per 100g clay. As would be expected from the absence of isomorphous substitution, the cation exchange capacity of pyrophyl-lites and talcs is very low. For montmorillonites the exchange capacities can be estimated from the approximate unit cell weight (see table 1.3) and from the layer charge per unit cell: the result is about 70–100 milliequivalents per 100g clay, in agreement with measured values. This agreement indicates that in montmorillonite the exchangeable cations located at all the charged sites are accessible for exchange with external ions in solution. The layer charge of vermiculites and micas is higher than that of montmorillonites; the exchange capacity would therefore be expected to increase in the order smectite $<$ vermiculite $<$ mica. The measured exchange capacities, however, are found to be highest for smectites such as montmorillonite, whereas the exchange capacities of micas are found to be lower. The explanation of the apparent anomaly is that in micas only the cations at the external surfaces of the crystals are exchangeable. In smectites, water molecules are able to penetrate between the unit layers; this results in an increase in the basal spacing to values between 1.2 and 1.8 nanometres or even higher. Due to this interlayer swelling, the exchangeable cations at charged sites in the interior of the crystal between the layers are accessible to cations in the solution for exchange. Micas do not swell in water, the basal spacing remains at about 1 nanometre and the cations located at interior unit layer surfaces are not readily exchangeable for ions in the external solution.

A second mechanism giving rise to charged sites on clay mineral surfaces in contact with water is the ionization of the alumina and silica groups at the edge (or prism) surfaces exposed to the aqueous solution. Whereas cleavage of a clay crystallite along basal surfaces does not involve the breaking of *primary valence bonds*, termination of the crystal at its edges does involve bond breakage of this kind. It is generally assumed that the exposed metal ions of the crystal edge (such as Si^{4+} and Al^{3+}) conserve their coordination, and complete their coordination shells by adsorption of hydrogen or hydroxyl ions or molecules of water from the solution. Thus, the sign of the charge of the edge surfaces of clay mineral crystallites depends on the pH of the solution surrounding the crystals. In this respect, the edge surfaces of clay crystallites behave like dispersions of silica and alumina. These oxides adsorb protons reversibly from solution at a certain pH, the oxide particles are uncharged: this pH is known as the *point of zero charge* (PZC) for the oxide. For aluminas, the PZCs are in the region of pH 9; for silicas, between pH 1 and 2. The edge surfaces of clay crystallites can be regarded as analogous to mixed aluminium silicates. For such materials it is more appropriate to refer to an isoelectric pH, or *isoelectric point*, rather than point of zero charge, because the surface of a mixed oxide is never devoid of all charge: it is the *net* electric charge that is zero at the isoelectric point. The isoelectric points of mixed oxides depend on the aluminium/silicon ratio in the oxide; at 50 per cent Al_2O_3 content, the isoelectric pH of synthetic aluminium silicates is about 6.5. The implication of this for soil clays is that over the whole pH range of interest for plant growth, the edge surfaces of clay minerals carry both positive and negative charges and can therefore retain both cations and anions. The importance of the edge surfaces is most pronounced for the kaolinite type clays in which the crystallites are thickest, so that the edge surface area contributes appreciably to the total surface area of the crystal.

The location of the exchangeable cations on the kaolinite crystal surface has been uncertain until recently. The extent of isomorphous substitution in this clay mineral is low (see table 1.4) and it is difficult to establish the actual extent unambiguously, because contaminating minerals are usually found even in the best kaolinite samples. It was therefore assumed until recently that the exchangeable cations of kaolinite are all located at the edges of the crystallites. When, however, measurements of the areas of the edge surfaces of this mineral were made, it became evident that it was *sterically* impossible to accommodate all the exchangeable cations at the edge surfaces even if they were allowed close packing. For this and other reasons it is now believed that the exchangeable cations of kaolinite are distributed over both the edge and the external basal surfaces. The ion-exchange properties of kaolinites are similar to those of micas in that only the external crystal surfaces are involved in ion exchange.

Isomorphous substitution in clay minerals is a more or less permanent lattice defect; the surface charge arising from this source is therefore not subject to variation with the properties of the external solution such as pH. It is also known, therefore, as the *pH-independent charge*. The ionization of the edge surfaces of clay minerals, on the other hand, does depend on the pH of the external solution: the edge surfaces become more negative with increasing pH and their ability to retain cations increases. This type of surface charge is referred to as the *pH-dependent charge*. As the total cation exchange capacity (CEC) is the sum of the pH independent and pH dependent negative charges, it also increases with pH. When measuring the CEC of a soil or clay it is therefore necessary to report the experimental pH; cation exchange capacities are normally measured at pH 7.

Ion exchange on clay minerals

Ion exchange has been the subject of much research ever since its discovery in the 1850s, because of its considerable theoretical and practical interest. It has been said to be of comparable importance to photosynthesis. Three aspects of the problem will be selected for brief discussion: the magnitude of the exchange capacity; the affinity of the ion exchange material for the different ions; and the rates of ion-exchange processes. *Cation exchange* will be considered first.

While the extent of isomorphous substitution or layer charge is a permanent and largely invariant property of a given clay mineral, the measured cation exchange capacity for any one clay mineral usually depends on the conditions under which the exchange capacity has been measured. There are several reasons for this. The number of charged sites on the edge surfaces of the clay crystallites varies with pH, as has already been mentioned. The nature, particularly the variable size, of the exchangeable ions on the exchanger or in the solution can lead to ion fixation, blockage of exchange sites or to incomplete replacement of one ion by another. Instances of *equimolar* rather than *equivalent* ion exchange have also been reported attending the exchange of monovalent cations by divalent ones. Whenever CECs are reported, the conditions of measurement should always be specified. The classical method of measuring the cation exchange capacity involves the conversion of the clay or soil into the *homoionic* form by washing with a concentrated electrolyte solution. The excess electrolyte is then removed with water or with aqueous ethanol. Finally the exchangeable cations retained by the clay from the electrolyte are removed by leaching with a second and different electrolyte solution, and the cations of the first electrolyte are assayed in the leachate by a suitable method. The electrolyte commonly used for saturating the clay is N ammonium acetate at pH 7; the exchangeable ammonium ions can be removed from the clay after ethanol washing by distillation as ammonia or by leaching the clay with a concentrated solution of a second electrolyte. The choice of the ammonium cation in CEC measurements was originally due to the lack of simple methods for the estimation of other monovalent cations such as sodium or potassium. With the development of flame photometry this restriction has now been removed. Estimates of CEC based on ammonium may be subject to errors due to fixation of ammonium by the clay. This will result in an underestimate of the CEC; alternatively, when ammonium is removed from the clay for analysis by distillation, the values will be overestimates due to the inclusion of adsorbed ammonia as distinct from exchangeable ammonium into the CEC.

With the advent of radioactive isotopes, an alternative method for the measurement of CEC is now available: the method of *isotopic dilution*. The clay or soil is first converted to the homoionic form and the excess electrolyte is removed as previously. The homoionic, electrolyte-free clay is then equilibrated with a labelled solution of the same salt containing a known ratio of labelled to non-labelled cations; in other words, it is of known *specific activity* $M*/M$ where $M*$ is the concentration of the radiotracer cation and M is the concentration of the same, non-labelled cation in the solution. The specific activity of the labelled electrolyte solution will decrease during equilibration with the clay because of dilution by the nonradioactive exchangeable cations. At equilibrium the specific activity of the experimental cation in solution and on the clay surface will be equal: $(M*/M)_{solution} = (M*/M)_{exchangeable}$. The specific activity of the labelled cation in solution can be measured directly; the amount of radiotracer adsorbed can be obtained by difference between the initial and final counts in the supernatant solution. The only remaining unknown is the amount of exchangeable cation on the clay which can be calculated.

This method is free from the ambiguities introduced by the use of a second electrolyte for the removal of exchangeable cations and by the use of distillation of ammonium as ammonia. It has been applied to clays using the radiosotope of calcium, Ca^{45}; but other isotopes such as Na^{22} or K^{42} could also be used.

Clay minerals, like other ion exchangers, vary in their preference for different ions. This preference is a reflexion of the differences between the energies of adsorption of the ions on the surface. While it is not possible to measure the energy of adsorption of a single ion, it is possible to obtain an estimate of the difference between the adsorption energies of a pair of ions at the clay mineral surface. An approximate measure of this difference is the *selectivity coefficient*, C_s. For an exchange of monovalent ions M^+ and N^+, the selectivity coefficient can be formulated as follows

$$M^+_{ads} + N^+_{soln} \rightleftharpoons M^+_{soln} + N^+_{ads}$$

$$C_s = \frac{M^+_{soln}/M^+_{ads}}{N^+_{soln}/N^+_{ads}}$$

where M^+ and N^+ are the concentrations of the two ions in solution or their equivalent fractions adsorbed on the exchanger. In the absence of selectivity the distribution ratios of the two monovalent ions between the exchanger and the solution are equal, that is $M^+_{soln}/M^+_{ads} = N^+_{soln}/N^+_{ads}$ and the value of the selectivity coefficient is unity. If the affinity of the exchanger is higher for N^+ than for M^+, the value of C_s is greater than 1; conversely a selectivity coefficient smaller than 1 indicates preference of the exchanger for M^+ over N^+. Experiments with clays and a range of monovalent ions have shown that the selectivity coefficient is only very approximately equal to 1, but it is almost constant for any one ion pair, irrespective of the equivalent fraction of ions adsorbed on the exchanger. A typical set of ion-exchange curves is shown in figure 1.5. The broken

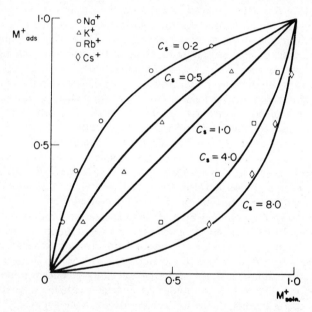

Figure 1.5 Ion-exchange curves for 1:1 valent ion exchange. M^+_{soln} and M^+_{ads} are the equivalent fractions of ammonium ion in solution and on the exchanger, respectively. The curves were calculated for various chosen C_S values. The experimental points are for exchange of ammonium (M^+) against some other monovalent ions (N^+).

Results of H. Martin and H. Laudelout, *J. Chim. Phys.*, **60** (1963) 1086.

line shows the hypothetical ion exchange isotherm corresponding to $C_s = 1$ (no selectivity). Typically, the affinity of clays for monovalent cations increases in the order $Li^+ < Na^+ < K^+ \leqslant NH_4^+ < Rb^+ < Cs^+$. Valency is therefore not the only property of an ion affecting the selectivity coefficient: when dealing with ions of the same valency, ion size is decisive. The order of affinities just given is also the order in which the hydrated ion size decreases. As the effective size of ions decreases, so does the distance of closest approach between the ion and the exchanger surface; it would be expected, therefore, that the energy of ion adsorption should also increase with decreasing ion size. The observed order of affinities indicates that the adsorbed ions retain their *hydration shells* when adsorbed on the exchanger.

Ion exchange between divalent—divalent ion pairs, such as Ca^{2+}/Mg^{2+}, would follow the same pattern as the monovalent—monovalent exchanges represented in figure 1.5. The case of monovalent—divalent exchanges, such as Na^{+}/Ca^{2+} is more complicated. Valency should have a major effect on the selectivity coefficient and, in the absence of other effects, the exchanger should have a higher affinity for the divalent ion than for the monovalent one. The expected distribution of divalent and monovalent ions between the exchanger and the solution can be worked out from the theoretical model of the *electrical double layer*. The electrical double layer at the surfaces of clay crystallites consists of the electrically charged clay surface (*the surface charge*) and a compensating layer of oppositely charged ions or counterions (*the volume charge*). The simplified model of the electrical double layer regards the ions as point charges: it neglects ion size. The charged surface is regarded as being flat, which is a good approximation for the basal surfaces of clays. Both the *density of surface charge* on the adsorbent and the *dielectric constant* of the surrounding electrolyte solution are taken to be continuous and uniform. The model takes into account the electrostatic interactions between the surface and the ions but not those between neighbouring adsorbed ions and the effect of thermal motion of the ions on the ion distribution.

Based on this simplified picture, the expected distribution of mono- and divalent ions between the exchanger and the solution can be worked out. Ion exchange curves for the monovalent—divalent exchange are given in figure 1.6, and show that the preference of the ion exchanger for the divalent ion should increase with the increase in concentration of the divalent ion in solution. It should also increase with the increase in surface charge density of the exchanger. Although the double-layer model used in arriving at these curves is rather oversimplified, comparisons of calculated selectivity coefficients with experimentally determined ones are useful because they indicate whether it is necessary to postulate the action of forces other than electrostatic ones (the only ones taken into account in the calculations) to explain the observable ion distributions. There are well-known cases, such as the K^{+}/Ca^{2+} or NH_4^{+}/Ca^{2+} exchange on micas and other clay minerals where the exchanger has a much higher affinity for the monovalent ions than it should have if only electrostatic forces were operating. This is then referred to as *specific adsorption* (or *fixation*) of potassium or ammonium. When the observed ion distribution agrees with the one expected from the theory of the electrical double layer, this may

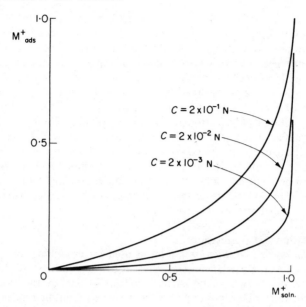

Figure 1.6 Ion-exchange curves for 2:1 valent ion exchange M^+_{soln} and M^+_{ads} are the equivalent fractions of the monovalent ion in solution and on the exchanger respectively.

The curves were calculated from the theory of the electrical double layer for various total electrolyte concentrations $C = c_1 + 2c_2$ assuming a surface charge density of 1.76×10^{-7} milliequivalents/cm^2 which corresponds to 17.6 milliequivalents/100 g for a specific surface area of 100 m^2/g.

be due to one of two reasons: either the corrections which have been neglected are small compared with the electrical forces determining the ion distribution, or there are several corrections acting in opposite directions whose effects tend to cancel.

In natural soils ion-exchange reactions are occurring continuously and the ion-exchange system is rarely at equilibrium. The rates of ion-exchange reactions are therefore also of interest. These reaction rates are relatively fast and their study has only recently been undertaken in detail. Generally, the ion-exchange rate was found to be controlled by the rate of diffusion of ions through the thin, stationary water layers surrounding the clay crystallites. The half-time of attainment of equilibrium was found to be about 1–3 minutes for kaolinite and 3–3000 minutes for montmorillonite, depending on the types of exchangeable ions used and on the free electrolyte concentration. The longer and more variable half-times of exchange for the expanding 2:1 layer clays reflect the prevalence of internal, intracrystalline surfaces in these clays; such surfaces are absent in 1:1 layer clays.

The discussion has so far been restricted to the exchange of cations. Anion exchange-like phenomena are also known to occur in soil clays: as there are positively charged sites on the edge surfaces of clay crystallites, this is not unexpected. Of the anions of importance in soils, clays have very low affinities for nitrate and chloride. These ions are normally regarded as not being adsorbed by clays, which is approximately true. The affinity of clays for the divalent sulphate anion is higher. Phosphate is known to be adsorbed strongly by clays and soils. This effect has been much studied due to the practical importance of phosphate fixation, but the mechanism of the processes involved is still controversial. Formation of surface complexes (*chemisorption*) of aluminium and ferric phosphate seems to be involved, rather than simple anion exchange. Anion exchange on soil clays is less reversible, and less stoichiometric than is cation exchange. Further work is needed in this area.

Flocculation and coagulation

Flocculation and *coagulation* are terms used for describing the process of aggregation of particles in clay suspensions and pastes. A flocculated system is one in which the particles adhere to one another, whereas in deflocculated suspensions or pastes the particles retain their independence. In a growth medium deflocculation is undesirable because of its adverse effect on the pore-size distribution. Individual clay crystallites tend to repack when deflocculated, thereby reducing the mean hydrodynamic pore radius in the growth medium and thus the rate of flow of water for infiltration and drainage.

Whether clay particles in a suspension or paste are flocculated or not depends on the balance of attractive and repulsive forces between the particles. The attractive forces are of the universal van der Waals type acting between all atoms, ions and molecules. The attractive force between two atoms falls off rapidly with the distance of separation: the attractive force is proportional to the inverse sixth power of the distance. The total attractive force between two clay platelets can be worked out by summing the attractive forces of the individual atoms. Such calculations show that the attractive force between two plates falls at a rate proportional to the inverse third power of the distance of separation when the plates are up to about 12 nm apart, and at a rate proportional to the inverse fourth power at plate distances larger than about 50 nm (so called *retarded van der Waals forces*). The attractive force between large particles is thus decreasing much more slowly with distance than the same force between two isolated atoms. The magnitude of the attractive force depends on the material of which the particles are made but it is largely independent of the concentration of the solution between the plates. The validity of these calculations has recently been supported by direct experimental measurements of the attractive force between platelets of mica.

The repulsive forces between clay platelets are electrostatic in nature and are due to the presence of the electrical double layer at the clay particle surface. When two clay platelets approach each other, their electrical double layers interpenetrate. This leads to a redistribution of ions in the double layer. The work required to bring about this redistribution gives rise to a repulsive force, which falls off approximately exponentially with distance of separation between the plates. Unlike the van der Waals attractive forces the repulsive forces are sensitive to the valency and concentration of the electrolyte between the clay particles. The attractive and repulsive forces between clay platelets, expressed as the corresponding attractive and repulsive energies of interaction, are shown in figure 1.7. As shown in this figure the effect of an increase in the valency

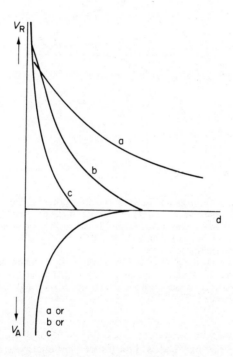

Figure 1.7 Schematic diagram showing the repulsive (V_R) and attractive (V_A) potential energies of interaction between clay platelets as a function of plate distance:

(a) for low electrolyte contentration, or for monovalent counterions; (b) for intermediate electrolyte concentration or for divalent counterions; (c) for high electrolyte concentration or for trivalent counterions.

The effect of increasing electrolyte concentration on the repulsive potential energy is similar to that of increasing counterion valency. The attractive potential energy is unaffected by these conditions.

of the counterions or of an increase in the concentration of counterions in the solution is to reduce the range of the repulsive force. To obtain the combined effects of the attractive and repulsive *energies of interaction* on the flocculation behaviour of clays, these energies, taken to have opposite signs, are summed for each particle separation. This gives the total potential energy curve for each particle separation. At low valency or low concentration of electrolyte (figure 1.8a), the total potential energy curve

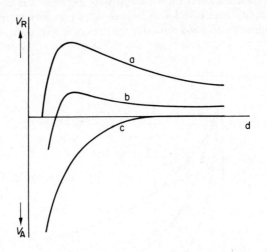

Figure 1.8 Schematic diagram showing the total potential energies of interaction between clay platelets as a function of plate distance: (a) for low electrolyte concentration or for monovalent counterions; (b) for intermediate electrolyte concentration or for divalent counterions; (c) for high electrolyte concentration or for trivalent counterions.

Curve (a) shows a high potential-energy barrier to flocculation, and the suspension is colloidally stable; in curve (b), the potential-energy barrier is low and allows slow flocculation; curve (c) shows no potential-energy barrier and represents a rapidly flocculating suspension.

has a maximum, which is referred to as a *potential energy barrier*. If this barrier is high, few particles will have sufficient energy to overcome it and encounters between particles will not lead to flocculation. However, in the absence of a potential energy barrier at high valency or high concentration of electrolyte (figure 1.8c), all particle encounters lead to flocculation. At intermediate electrolyte concentrations slow flocculation occurs (figure 1.8b), since only a fraction of encounters between particles is effective.

These considerations provide a qualitative explanation for the observed flocculation-deflocculation phenomena in saline soils, such as those reclaimed from the sea. As long as the soil is in contact with seawater, the concentration of electrolyte (mainly sodium chloride) at the surfaces of soil clays is high and the soil remains flocculated. Partial or complete removal of sodium ions from the soil by leaching often leads to deflocculation: under these conditions, the soils are sticky, their permeability to water and air is low and they are physically unmanageable. The situation can be improved by introducing flocculating ions, such as calcium; this is often done by applying gypsum (calcium sulphate). Lime (calcium carbonate) acts similarly, but improvement in the physical conditions is then usually slow because of the low solubility of this compound.

Flocculation of soil clays, as discussed so far, depends on the compression of the electrical double layer by electrolytes. Such flocculation is reversible in that the clay can be deflocculated if the electrolyte solution in contact with the clay is replaced by one with ions of lower valency or concentration. Another, somewhat different way of flocculating or deflocculating clays is by treatment with *polyelectrolytes*. These are large, usually but not necessarily organic molecules with many ionized groups. When these ionized groups are positively charged, the polyelectrolyte is said to be a *polycation*; on *polyanions* the ionized groups are negatively charged. Polycations are usually good flocculants: under suitable conditions each polycation adsorbs onto more than one clay particle, forming cross-links between these particles. Polyanions may also act as flocculants, either by adsorption on positive sites on the clay and cross-linking or by partially neutralizing polyvalent exchangeable cations on more than one clay particle. Polyanions can also act as powerful deflocculating agents under certain conditions. This happens when each polyanion adsorbs on a single clay particle and thus increases the net negative charge of this particle. Flocculation by polyelectrolytes is a much less reversible process than that due to simple electrolytes. Flocculation by simple salts is therefore sometimes referred to as *coagulation* to distinguish it from flocculation brought about by polymer bridging.

Native soil organic matter behaves in many ways as a polyelectrolyte and its importance in maintaining soil aggregation is now well recognized. Polyuronides, such as alginic or pectic acids, and polysaccharide products which are present in soil organic matter are all known to improve the state of soil aggregation, even though the effect is often only rather temporary. Synthetic polyelectrolytes, known as *soil conditioners*, have also been produced industrially in the hope of producing more reproducible and longer lasting effects. The polymer backbone of these soil conditioners is usually some derivative of polyacrylonitrile or of polymethyl methacrylate (figure 1.9). Carboxyl groups may be introduced into the polymers to yield polyanions; polycationic soil conditioners usually carry amino groups. Two representative polyelectrolytes (one anionic, the other cationic) are also shown in figure 1.9. Although soil conditioners do improve soil aggregation when applied appropriately, they have not found general application due to their relatively high cost. However, under

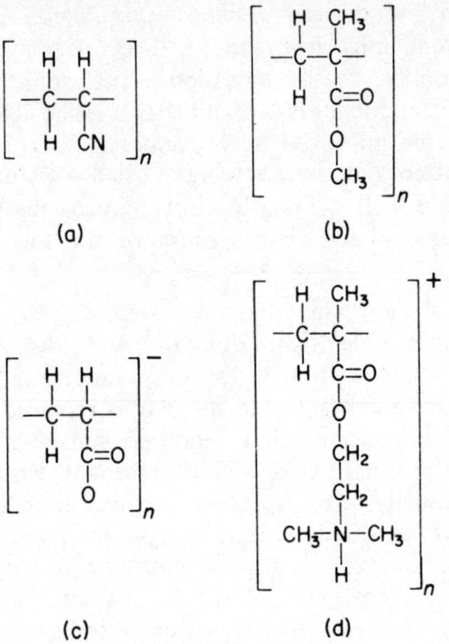

(a)   (b)

(c)   (d)

Figure 1.9 Some representative soil conditioners: (a) polyacrylonitrile; (b) polymethyl methacrylate; (c) hydrolysed polyacrylonitrile anion; (d) polydimethyl–2–aminoethylmethacrylate cation.

specialized conditions, such as to prevent capping of clayey soils and to improve germination, their use may be justified.

The nature of water at clay surfaces

The properties of water turn out to be quite unusual when compared with those of chemically related compounds (table 1.6). This is well illustrated by the melting point of ice and the boiling point of water. The melting and boiling points, which are much higher than the corresponding temperatures of transition for related dihydrides, indicate that strong attractive forces operate between molecules of water. The intermolecular

Table 1.6

Melting and boiling points for water and some related dihydrides

	Melting point (°C)	Boiling point (°C)
Water (H_2O)	0.0	100.0
Hydrogen sulphide (H_2S)	−85.5	−60.7
Hydrogen selenide (H_2Se)	−60.4	−41.5
Hydrogen telluride (H_2Te)	−49	−2

forces arise from the dipolar nature of the water molecule. Although it is electrically neutral overall, the water molecule is electrically asymmetrical: the more electronegative oxygen atom attracts the electrons from the two hydrogen atoms. Thus the oxygen atom of water is the seat of a partial local negative charge, while the hydrogen atoms carry partial positive charges (figure 1.10). The electrostatic attraction between the partial

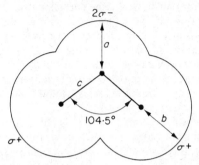

Figure 1.10 Structure of the water molecule. σ^+ and σ^- are partial positive and negative charges, equivalent to 6.9 per cent of the charge on the electron. a = van der Waals radius of oxygen: 140 pm; b = van der Waals radius of hydrogen: 120 pm; c = O—H covalent bond length: 96.5 pm.

negative charge on the oxygen atom of one water molecule and the partial positive charges on hydrogen atoms of other water molecules is known as *hydrogen bonding*. In ice each water molecule is hydrogen bonded to four nearest neighbours arranged tetrahedrally. The hydrogen-bond energy in water, the energy required to break the bonds, is 38 kJ/mole (9 kcal/mole). As every molecule has a half-share in four hydrogen bonds, the hydrogen bond energy is 19 kJ (4.5 kcal) per 'mole hydrogen bond', much lower than the covalent bond energy between oxygen and hydrogen (460 kJ/mole $\equiv$ 110 kcal/mole). The heat of fusion of water is 6.05 kJ/mole (1.44 kcal/mole), only 16 per cent of the hydrogen-bond energy per mole of water. Thus, liquid water retains a high degree of hydrogen bonding which persists, although to a lesser extent, even in the vapour phase. Only at about 600°C are all the hydrogen bonds broken in water vapour.

Water may interact with clay surfaces in different ways. The layer of water molecules nearest to the clay surface will tend to hydrogen bond with the oxygen atoms of the surface. This hydrogen bonding would be enhanced by partial overlap of the hexagonal pattern of oxygen atoms in the clay surface with similar patterns in the partially hydrogen-bonded water structure and also by the excess electrons in the clay surface. These excess electrons, present as a result of *isomorphous substitution*, promote the formation of stronger, more covalent hydrogen bonds between the oxygen atoms of the clay surface and the hydrogen atoms of water. These relatively strong, partially covalent hydrogen bonds also tend to facilitate the formation of further such bonds in a cooperative manner in the next layer of adsorbed water molecules. This process may lead to the build-up of many layers of water hydrogen-bonded to the clay surface and held together by further hydrogen bonds of decreasing covalency.

The adsorbed water is therefore likely to be structured, though the prevailing structure is unlikely to be that of ice. This may be partly due to the lack of exact overlap between the surface patterns of oxygen atoms and the tetrahedral water structure and also to the presence of the exchangeable cations at the clay surface. These ions are also hydrated and would tend to disrupt the ordered arrangement of the adsorbed water layers especially if they were of small radius and of multiple valence. In addition to hydrogen bonding and counterion hydration forces, the general van der Waals attractive forces would also contribute to the adsorption of water onto clay surfaces.

The extent to which liquid water is hydrogen bonded in the $0°C-100°C$ temperature range is known only approximately. Thus it is not surprising that there should be some divergence of opinion on the much more complicated question of the structure of water adsorbed at clay surfaces and on the distance to which the ordered structure extends from the clay surface. Some workers believe that this order extends to several tens of molecular layers of water; others think it is restricted to the first few water layers only. The answer to the question would be of some interest because the thickness of the water layers on clays in growth media with optimal moisture contents for plant growth happens to be intermediate between the two limits indicated.

1.3   AMORPHOUS INORGANIC SOIL MATERIALS

Prior to about 1930, when evidence from X-ray diffraction first showed that the clay fraction of soils contains much crystalline material, it was generally believed that the whole of the colloidal fraction of soils is *amorphous*. X-ray diffraction techniques then gave a boost to the study of soil clay minerals, and the inorganic amorphous materials were, until recently, comparatively neglected. The division of the inorganic clay fraction into crystalline and amorphous materials is now seen to be neither fundamental nor clear cut. This is due partly to continuous improvements in the methods for detecting regularities in the structure of materials. These developments increase the number of materials that are regarded as crystalline at the expense of the group classified as amorphous. Moreover, the edge surfaces of clay crystallites behave in many ways as mixed amorphous oxides of aluminium and silicon; the atomic composition of such surfaces is not unlike that of some amorphous aluminosilicates known to occur in some soils. For practical reasons, however, it still seems justified to discuss the groups of crystalline and amorphous inorganic soil materials separately.

The amorphous inorganic materials in the clay fraction of soils are usually hydrous oxides of iron, aluminium, silicon or manganese, occurring either separately or combined, and often containing phosphate as well. The iron and aluminium oxides extractable from soils are often referred to as 'free oxides' and are taken to represent amorphous material. This usage is inaccurate since the material extracted need have been neither free nor amorphous in the soil solid phase. The terminology used to describe the amorphous oxides occurring in soils is somewhat ill-defined, as are the materials themselves. Some mineral names and compositions in use for materials found in amorphous mineral deposits are collected in table 1.7.

Table 1.7

Nomenclature for amorphous hydrous oxides and hydroxides †

Name	Formula
Opaline silica	$SiO_2.nH_2O$
Limonite	$Fe_2O_3.nH_2O$
Kliachite	$Al_2O_3.nH_2O$
Allophane	$Al_2O_3.2SiO_2.nH_2O$
Hisingerite	$Fe_2O_3.2SiO_2.nH_2O$
Evansite	$Al_3PO_4(OH)_6.nH_2O$
Azovskite	$Fe_3PO_4(OH)_6.nH_2O$

† See reference 6 for this chapter.

Alpha quartz is the most common crystalline form of silica in soils; opaline silica differs from quartz in that it is amorphous and has a lower density. Iron oxides may occur both in crystalline and in amorphous forms; the distinction is a difficult one to make experimentally because the crystalline forms are often disordered. The amorphous forms of iron oxide occur mostly in highly leached soils either as discrete particles or as coatings on clay crystallites. They often determine the colour of the soil. Most work has concentrated on the techniques for the removal of amorphous iron oxides from soil samples rather than on the elucidation of their nature. Amorphous aluminium hydroxides are also associated with extensive weathering. They may occur in the interlayer space of expanded 2:1 layer clays. These forms are intermediate between the 2:1 layer clay minerals and chlorite (see table 1.4). The usage of the term 'allophane' is rather confused: sometimes it is meant to cover any amorphous material of indefinite composition in the clay fraction of soils, but occasionally its use is restricted to hydrated aluminosilicates of more or less fixed composition (table 1.7). Allophane has been studied most extensively in the recent volcanic deposits of New Zealand and Japan, where it is the dominant mineral in the clay fraction of many soils.

The cation-exchange capacity of allophane-rich clays can be high; values up to 40—60 meq per 100 g clay have been reported. The cation-exchange capacity (CEC) is more dependent on the conditions of the measurement with amorphous clays than with crystalline ones. It is particularly sensitive to pH and is much reduced between pH 7 and 5, whereas the anion-exchange capacity is simultaneously increased. This effect is similar to that described in connection with ion exchange at the edge surfaces of crystalline clays.

The most successful method available for the characterization of crystalline clay minerals, X-ray diffraction, is of limited use with amorphous materials. Other methods, such as *differential thermal analysis, infrared spectroscopy* and electron microscopy are, however, just as useful as with crystalline clays. A combination of these methods, together with chemical analyses and differential dissolution techniques, are now used to improve our understanding of these soil constituents.

1.4   ORGANIC SOIL MATERIALS

Crystallinity confers considerable advantages on materials from the point of view of structure analysis. The atomic positions in molecules of even great complexity (such as proteins) can now be mapped in detail using powerful diffraction methods. These same methods are, however, of little use with materials of limited crystallinity. Soil organic matter, in addition to appearing amorphous, is variable in composition and the separation from whole soils and other growth media such as peats is difficult without causing changes in the extracted material. Thus, in spite of continued research efforts extending over a hundred years, the nature of much of the organic material of soils is still obscure. Nevertheless the importance of organic matter in maintaining the productivity of soils, and the use of predominantly organic materials such as peat as main or as accessory components of growth media, justify a brief review of the present state of knowledge in this field.

Discussion will be restricted to humic substances. Non-humic organic materials (such as proteins, fats, carbohydrates and low molecular weight substances of microbial, animal or plant origin) also occur in soils but their turnover is usually rapid. Humic substances are the relatively stable, acidic, yellow-brown to black organic polymers of non-constant molecular weight found in soils and peats. The usual separation techniques of organic chemistry and biochemistry (such as chromatography and electrophoresis) have so far not produced homogeneous fractions from any humic materials. It has been suggested that no two molecules of humic substance may be exactly alike. While this makes studies of humic materials more difficult, it does not preclude proper scientific investigations; no two clay crystallites are exactly alike, either. Based on solubilities, it has been customary to divide the group into three subgroups: *fulvic acids, humic acids* and *humins.* Fulvic acids are soluble in both acids and alkalis and are of relatively low molecular weight; humic acids are soluble in alkalis but not in acids and are of intermediate molecular weight; humins are said to have the highest molecular weights and are soluble in alkalis only with difficulty. The divisions are somewhat arbitrary, however, as there seems to be continuous gradation between the subgroups.

Characterization of polymeric materials usually begins with degradation into lower molecular weight forms which can then be separated and characterized. A picture of the original polymer is then assembled from the information on the fragments. The difficulty with degradative procedures for humic substances is that they are either too mild to produce substantial amounts of lower molecular weight fragments or too drastic, decomposing the humic materials into small molecules (like H_2O, CO_2 and NH_3), which are of no value for structure analyses. Acid hydrolysis releases only small amounts of amino acids and little, if any, carbohydrates. The latter are therefore not regarded as part of the molecular structure of humic substances. Alkaline hydrolysis releases phenolic substances without completely breaking down the central parts of the molecules. Oxidation, particularly with nitric acid, and reduction have also been used to degrade humic substances prior to analysis.

The number and type of functional groups (such as carboxyl, hydroxyl and carbonyl groups) on humic substances have been estimated in several ways, but the results are often difficult to interpret. These difficulties are not unexpected as the materials under study are heterogeneous. The different reactive groups on the polymers interact with each other. The total acidity as measured by functional group analysis is of interest as it is related to the cation exchange capacity of the humic material. Spectroscopic methods (for example, *infrared* and *nuclear magnetic resonance*) are nondestructive techniques widely used in organic chemistry for characterizing organic molecules: infrared spectroscopy to reveal the presence of individual bonds, and the different magnetic resonance techniques for characterizing free radicals and protons. The usefulness of these techniques increases with the purity of the preparation to which they are applied, and would therefore be used to obtain additional information on molecules already characterized by other methods.

Observations made in different laboratories on humic substances are sometimes conflicting. Certain results have, however, come to be generally accepted. The molecular weights of humic substances vary from about 2000 to over 300 000; both limits are somewhat arbitrary and depend on the techniques used for extraction of the humic materials from the growth medium. The mean molecular weight of a fraction is a useful characteristic, because it appears to be roughly correlated with other properties of the humic substance; it is unlikely to be of fundamental importance by itself, however, because no monodisperse fractions have so far been obtained from any humic material.

The elemental composition of humic material is variable. The carbon content varies from 45 to 65 per cent, increasing with molecular weight. The oxygen content, on the other hand, decreases with increasing molecular weight and is of the order of 30 to 50 per cent. The oxygen atoms are located partly in reactive functional groups (such as the carboxyl and hydroxyl groups) and partly in nonreactive positions (such as carbonyl groups, ether bonds and as parts of heterocyclic rings). The nitrogen content varies between 2 and 6 per cent, part of which is located in amino acids and the rest in the acid-resistant central structural units of the humic molecules. The hydrogen content is usually about 5 per cent.

The presence of several types of functional groups in humic substances has been demonstrated. Acidity is due to carboxyl groups and hydroxyl groups, probably present in about equal numbers. The ion-exchange capacity, which at pH 7 is mainly due to the carboxyl groups, varies from 500 milliequivalents per 100 g (for the lower molecular weight fractions) to about 170 milliequivalents per 100 g (for the higher molecular weights). The colour of humic substances is thought to be due to the conjugation of quinonic $C=O$ groups with $C=C$ bonds. The presence of unsaturated bonds (for example $C=C$) is also indicated by the results of halogenation and hydrogenation.

Humic substances are generally fairly resistant to acid hydrolysis and to microbial attack, but sensitive to even mild oxidizing agents. This indicates the absence of carbohydrates and of very stable aromatic compounds; small amounts of amino acids are usually present in acid hydrolysates. Alkali hydrolysis and (to a lesser extent) oxidation, reduction and acid hydrolysis release up to about 25 per cent of the humic substances as

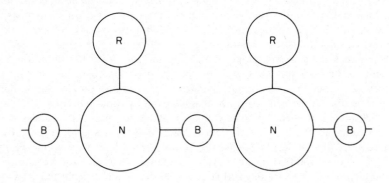

Figure 1.11   Generalized postulated structure of humic substances: N = nucleus of polymer molecule; R = reactive group; B = bridging group.
See reference 8 for this chapter.

phenolic compounds of microbial or plant origin. The information at present available indicates that the generalized structure of humic substances may consist of nuclei-bearing reactive groups, connected by bridge elements, as indicated in figure 1.11. A list of some possible nuclei, reactive groups and bridge units is presented in table 1.8. Several more or less specific schemes, based on limited experimental data, have from time to time been proposed in attempts to designate the nuclei, the bridge units and the manner of the cross-linking. None of them has gained wide acceptance. The question of the general structure of soil humic substances, including the degree of order in such a structure, is still wide open.

Table 1.8

Possible components of humic substances† (see chapter 1, reference 8)

Nucleus‡		Reactive group‡	Bridge unit‡
Benzene		— COOH	— O —
Naphthalene		— OH	— NH —
		$C=O$	$= N —$
Anthracene		— NH_2	— CH_2 —
Furan		— CH_3	
Thiophene		$-\overset{O}{\underset{OH}{S}}=O$	
Pyrrole			
Pyridine		$-\overset{O}{\underset{OH}{P}}-OH$	
Quinoline		$—OCH_3$	
Indole			

† See reference 8 for this chapter.

‡ A given bridge or reactive group is not necessarily associated with the nucleus on the same horizontal line.

1.5   CLAY–ORGANIC COMPLEXES

Organic and inorganic soil materials have so far been discussed independently. The clay fraction of most soils, however, consists of intimately associated organic and inorganic materials and separation, when required, is very difficult. Organo-mineral complexes, and the combinations and interactions of clay minerals with organic materials in particular, have for long been subjects of research. Clay mineral-organic interactions are of interest for several reasons. Under practical conditions it is the associations of the natural soil humic materials and of synthetic soil conditioners with clay minerals that determine the stability of soil aggregates. Adsorption usually protects organic molecules from decomposition: the organic matter and clay contents of soils are often positively related. Biologically active synthetic organic molecules (such as pesticides and herbicides) when applied to soils, react with the soil clays. Such reactions may immobilize the organic compound and render it temporarily inactive, although activity may be restored on desorption from the clay. Some compounds are catalytically decomposed at clay surfaces, thus permanently losing their biological activity.

Experimental study of clay mineral–organic complexes usually involves the study of the interaction of organic molecules of known structure with well-defined clay minerals, or the extraction of humic materials from soils followed by studying their reactions with clay minerals. Work of this kind has led to a better understanding of the mechanisms of interaction between clays and the adsorbed organic molecules, and of the nature of the resulting clay-organic complexes.

Commonly, more than one type of force contributes to the adsorption of an organic molecule onto the surface of a clay crystal. The commonest mechanism of adsorption is that of cation exchange. Positive charge on an organic molecule R is often due to the presence of an ionized· amino group, $-NH_3^+$

$$M^+clay + RNH_3^+ \rightleftharpoons RNH_3^+clay + M^+$$

The organic cation displaces another cation, M^+, at the negatively charged surface sites of the clay. The affinity of the clay depends on the exchangeable cations initially saturating the clay, and on the properties of the organic cation and of the clay. It is found in general that the monovalent sodium ion is much more easily replaced by alkylammonium ions than is the divalent calcium ion; the calcium ion is in turn more easily replaced than the trivalent aluminium ion. Organic cations affect the affinity for adsorption in different ways according to their type. The extent to which the organic molecule is charged (or ionized) depends on the pH. Contributions to the adsorption by forces other than ionic will also be important. Normally the affinity of a clay for organic cations increases with the molecular weight of the cation. This is due to the increased contribution of the noncoulombic, hydrophobic forces between the adsorbed molecules to the total energy of adsorption. The affinity for adsorption will also be affected by the type of clay and in particular, the relationship between the charge pattern on the clay and that on the adsorbed organic cation. This can be shown by comparing the adsorption of cations which differ only with respect to the distance separating their charged groups. A particular clay will prefer the organic cation, the ionized groups of which can get nearest to the charged sites on the crystal surface.

Another factor contributing to the adsorption of organic cations on clays is the supply of hydrogen ions available at the clay surface for protonating the adsorbate. A clay surface is usually much more acidic than the bulk solution with which it is in contact. The excess protons available at the clay surface may be present as exchangeable hydrogen ions; the reaction is then simply

$$H^+ clay + RNH_2 \rightleftharpoons RNH_3^+ clay$$

Another source of hydrogen ions for protonating bases is the water of hydration of exchangeable metallic cations. The more electronegative exchangeable cations, such as Al^{3+} or Fe^{3+} tend to hydrolyse at the clay surface and release protons

$$Al (H_2O)_n^{3+} \rightleftharpoons [AlOH(H_2O)_{n-1}]^{2+} + H^+$$

The hydrogen ions released then protonate the organic base. The extent of this reaction depends on the relative affinities of the exchangeable cation for electrons and of the base for protons. Strong bases (such as ammonia), which have a high affinity for protons, will take these from the hydration shells of exchangeable calcium, or even sodium ions. Weak bases (like urea) will only be protonated by hydrogen, aluminium or ferric ions at clay surfaces. The acidic form of a base AH^+ already adsorbed can also yield hydrogen ions for protonating a base B stronger than itself

$$AH^+ + B \rightleftharpoons BH^+ + A$$

The adsorption of polar, but nonionic, molecules onto clay surfaces is also well established. A selection of such molecules is given in table 1.9. Some of these substances (such as ammonia and urea) have recently become of direct practical interest as fertilizers, now being applied on a large scale. These polar molecules are adsorbed primarily by displacing water from the hydration shells of exchangeable cations M^+ at the clay surface. The reaction can be described as a 'solvation' of the exchangeable cation by the polar organic molecule. For an alcohol this solvation reaction occurs as follows

$$M(H_2O)_x^{n+} + y\, ROH \rightleftharpoons M(ROH)_y^{n+} + x\, H_2O$$

The tendency for adsorption by this mechanism will depend on the affinity of the exchangeable cations on the clay for the electrons donated

Table 1.9

Some classes of polar molecules known to form
adsorption complexes with clays

Compound	Formula
Ammonia	NH_3
Ketones	$R-\overset{\overset{\textstyle O}{\|\|}}{C}-R'$
Alcohols	$R-OH$
Urea	$NH_2-\overset{\overset{\textstyle O}{\|\|}}{C}-NH_2$
Amides	$RCONH_2$
Amines	$R-NH_2, R_2 NH, R_3 N$
Pyridine	
Nitrobenzene	$-NO_2$
Amino acids	$NH_2-\overset{\overset{\textstyle R}{\|}}{\underset{\underset{\textstyle H}{\|}}{C}}-COOH$

by the polar molecule. Transition metal cations will more readily be solvated by the organic molecules than divalent or monovalent ones.

Hydrogen bonding can also contribute to the adsorption of organic molecules by clays. The adsorbed molecules may be hydrogen bonded to the oxygens or hydroxyls of the clay surfaces, to the water molecules in the hydration shells of the exchangeable cations, or even to each other. The effect of the universal van der Waals attractive forces also becomes of importance especially for large molecules.

Covalent bonds between surface silanol groups ($\equiv Si - OH$) and organic compounds can also be prepared in the laboratory; such compounds, however, have not been found to occur naturally.

It is reasonably well established that humic and fulvic acids may adsorb on the external surfaces of clays. The adsorption seems to be most pronounced on amorphous clays such as allophane. It has also been observed that high allophane content is often related to high organic matter content in soils. The evidence regarding the presence or absence of fulvic and humic acids in the interlayer regions of clays is conflicting. Some investigators believe that humic materials do not penetrate the internal surfaces of clays. Others have apparently demonstrated that fulvic acids do enter the interlamellar region of montmorillonite. With increasing amounts of fulvic acid adsorbed, the basal spacing of the clay was observed to expand from 1.50 nm to 1.76 nm. Adsorption appeared to be strongly pH dependent and was favoured at low pH, around 2.5; it was, however, found to persist, though to a lesser extent, at pH values as high as 6.0. The type of exchangeable cation on the clay was also found to be important. Humic materials are, of course, anionic at all pH values, though less so at low pH values than at high ones. This would not favour their adsorption onto the negatively charged interlayer surfaces of montmorillonite. It is apparent from the foregoing discussion, however, that there are other mechanisms (such as hydrogen bonding, coordination to exchangeable cations or van der Waals forces) which could provide sufficient energy to overcome the coulombic repulsion of negative charges and allow the interlayer adsorption of fulvic or humic acid anions.

SUMMARY

Consideration of volume/surface relationships of soil particles shows that much of the surface area of soil solids is associated with the colloidal or clay fraction. Most of the immediate reserves of plant nutrients are located in or near the soil particle surfaces. It is therefore justified to concentrate the discussion of soil microstructure on the materials in the clay fraction.

The best-characterized components of the clay fraction are the group of layer silicates known as clay minerals. Crystal structures for the main types of clay minerals were first suggested by Pauling in the early 1930s. These structures have since been confirmed and refined primarily by X-ray diffraction methods. Clay mineral crystallites are usually plate or lath shaped and consist of stacks of unit layers. Each unit layer, about 1 nanometre in thickness, is made up of two or more silica and aluminium- or magnesium hydroxide layers. The unit layers are held together internally by strong valence bonds. The forces between neighbouring unit layers are the much weaker van der Waals forces and hydrogen bonds. The structure of some clay minerals is electrically neutral, but in most of them extensive substitution of cations of higher valency by those of lower valency occurs. This isomorphous substitution results in a net negative charge on the structure, which is neutralized by cations adsorbed from the external solution; the cations external to the unit layers are the exchangeable cations. Both cations and anions are also adsorbed at the edges of the clay crystallites where unit layers terminate.

Ion exchange on soil materials — a process of fundamental importance for plant nutrition — is characteristic of clay minerals; it is also characteristic of the amorphous inorganic and the organic materials in the clay fraction. This process refers to the exchange of ions adsorbed primarily by electrostatic forces at the surfaces of soil particles by ions of like charge from the soil solution. Ion exchange in soils primarily involves cations; the role of anion exchange is relatively minor. The value of exchangeable cations for plants is related to the rapidity of cation exchange processes. The presence of electrical charges on soil particles and the concentration and types of ions in the soil solution also determine the balance of attractive and repulsive forces between the soil particles and thus their tendency for flocculation or deflocculation. The state of flocculation is related to the macroscopic physical properties of the soil such as permeability and surface capping.

The composition and structure of the amorphous inorganic and of the organic soil materials is less well known, but their importance in cation exchange and in maintaining favourable physical conditions in soils is well established. Most natural soils consist of an intimate mixture of clay minerals and of soil organic matter. The structure of these mixed materials is not known in detail, but a wide range of well-defined clay-organic complexes with organic molecules sandwiched between the unit layers of clays has been prepared and studied.

CHAPTER 2

THE MOLECULAR ENVIRONMENT
OF PLANT ROOTS

Having reviewed the microstructure of soil materials, we shall now consider the pore space in growth media. Apart from the roots of plants this pore space contains the soil solution and the soil air. The components, to a first approximation, are water and the common atmospheric gases nitrogen, oxygen, water vapour and carbon dioxide. The solution in the pore space is of course not pure water but contains ions, some of which serve as nutrients for plants. For the purposes of this chapter, however, the presence of dissolved ions can be neglected except in so far as they affect the osmotic pressure of the soil solution, which is the case in saline soils. The pore space of a good growth medium allows the simultaneous presence of water and oxygen in adequate quantities around the roots of plants and it permits the movement of water and air at adequate rates in the plant root environment. There also are requirements with regards to the energy with which a good growth medium retains water over the widest possible range of moisture contents. The energy of water retention should not be excessive, because plants would then be unable to utilize the soil water. Nor should it be too small to prevent undue drainage by gravity. In the soil air the component of primary interest for plant roots is oxygen; the partial pressure of oxygen in the soil air should therefore be adequate for the requirements of plants. In this chapter we shall discuss the nature of the forces of attraction between soil and water; the different ways in which the energy of water retention can be expressed and measured; the principal methods for measuring the moisture content of soils; the factors affecting the rate of movement of water in soils; and some aspects of soil aeration.

2.1 THE FORCES OF WATER RETENTION IN SOILS

The simplest variable associated with soil-water status is the moisture content of the soil; while this is a useful quantity it is by no means sufficient to characterize the moisture status of a soil. It is common experience that one growth medium, such as a sandy soil, may support adequate plant growth at a given moisture content, while plants in another growth medium, such as a clay soil, containing the same percentage moisture may be failing or showing distress symptoms which can be relieved by the addition of water to the soil. These observations imply that water is more 'available' to plants in the first growth medium than in the second. There can be two reasons for this: either the energy of attraction between water and the soil components is too great to be overcome by plant roots in the second growth medium, or the rate at which water can reach the roots of the plant in the second growth medium is lower than the rate of evaporation of water from the plant to the atmosphere. Of course, both causes could be operative simultaneously. These considerations lead to the question: what is the nature of the attractive forces between soil and water?

The most general type of attraction between water and all porous media, including soils, arises as a result of the *surface tension* at the curved interfaces between air and water in the soil pores. Surface tension, or, more exactly, interfacial tension, arises from the asymmetric attractive forces to which molecules in the surface of a condensed phase, in particular a liquid phase, are subject (figure 2.1).

Gas phase

Surface

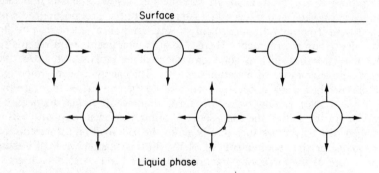

Liquid phase

Figure 2.1 Intermolecular attractive forces shown as arrows in the interior and at the surface of a liquid; molecules shown as circles.

In the interior of a liquid the short-range attractive forces acting on each molecule are balanced. The molecules at the surface of the liquid are, however, in an asymmetrical force field; the attractive forces are concentrated on the liquid side and are much weaker on the opposite side of the interface. The net result of this is that molecules have a tendency to move away from the surface into the interior of the liquid and that it requires work to extend the surface of the liquid. The energy associated with the formation of a unit area of new surface is the *surface energy*. Another equivalent concept is that of the surface tension. This is the force of attraction experienced along a unit length in a liquid surface (figure 2.2).

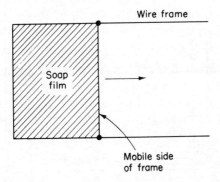

Figure 2.2   The equivalent concepts of surface energy and surface tension.
The force per unit length acting in the soap film on the mobile side of the wire frame in the direction opposing the arrow is the *surface tension*. The work done against this force when increasing the area of the soap film by one unit is the *surface energy*.

When the liquid surface is mobile and can alter its shape, the existence of surface tension has further macroscopically observable consequences. Under certain circumstances liquids have a tendency to form spheres; spherical geometry confers the minimum surface area on a body of given volume. A spherical soap bubble of radius r, for instance, will decrease in volume until, at equilibrium, the excess pressure ΔP building up inside the bubble exactly compensates for the effect of the surface tension (γ) tending to compress the sphere: $\Delta P = 2\gamma/r$. This expression is a simple form of what is known as the *Young–Laplace equation*. It shows that the pressure on either side of a curved liquid–air interface always differs, and in such a way that the pressure is greater on the concave side of the interface than on the convex side.

The existence of a pressure difference across curved air–water interfaces according to the Young–Laplace equation also explains the commonly observed phenomenon of *capillary rise*. If the liquid wets the surface of a capillary tube, the surface of the liquid will lie parallel to the wall and the shape of the whole air–water interface (figure 2.3a, dashed line) will therefore be concave, as seen from the air above the meniscus. The pressure on the convex (water) side of the interface will then be lower than on the concave (air) side and the liquid in the capillary will rise (meniscus in figure 2.3a). At equilibrium the pressure difference across the curved interface will be equal to the hydrostatic pressure of the liquid column in the capillary

$$\Delta P = 2\gamma/r = \rho g\, h$$

where ρ is the density of the water, g the gravitational constant and h the height of liquid in the capillary. If the liquid does not wet the wall of the

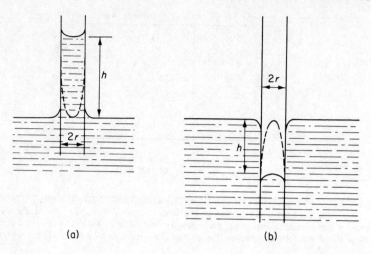

Figure 2.3 (a) The shape of an air–water interface in a glass capillary; the liquid wets the walls. (b) The shape of an air–mercury interface in the glass capillary; the liquid does not wet the walls.
At equilibrium, the capillary rise or depression is *h* cm.

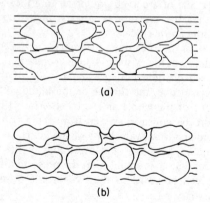

Figure 2.4 (a) In a saturated soil there are no curved air–water interfaces. (b) An unsaturated soil contains many curved air–water interfaces.

capillary (figure 2.3b, dashed line), the shape of the air—liquid interface formed will be convex as seen from the air above the meniscus, with excess pressure on the liquid side of the interface. The liquid will therefore drop in the capillary and at equilibrium the position of the meniscus will be as shown in figure 2.3b, with $\Delta P = 2\gamma/r = -\rho g h$. This is the phenomenon of *capillary depression* as would be exhibited by mercury in a glass capillary.

As a first approximation it can be assumed that the soil-pore space consists of a network of interconnected capillaries of continuously varying sizes and that the water wets the walls of these capillaries. In a completely saturated soil there is virtually no air-space (figure 2.4a) and thus no curved air—water interfaces. Surface tension therefore contributes nothing to water retention in a saturated soil. As the moisture content of the soil is reduced, however, curved air—water interfaces of varying radii are created in the soil pores (figure 2.4b). The water is then on the convex side of an air—water interface and thus under negative pressure (less than atmospheric) or suction; therefore work needs to be done to remove further water from the soil. This mode of water retention, due to capillary forces and related to the surface tension of water and to the radii of soil pores, is of general significance in all unsaturated soils and other porous media.

Water is also held in most soils by *osmotic forces*. These forces are due to the presence of ions, which can be either freely diffusible ions in the soil solution or ions adsorbed onto the surfaces of soil particles. It is well known that if a solution is separated from the solvent (for example, pure water) by a semipermeable membrane, water will tend to flow across the membrane into the solution. This observation can be explained by considering that the number of encounters between a unit surface of the membrane and water molecules is greater on the pure-water side of the membrane than on the solution side. The net flow stops eventually when the pressure of the excess water molecules on the solution side becomes

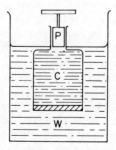

Figure 2.5 Schematic diagram of a simple osmometer, immersed in pure water W containing a solution of concentration c and fitted with piston P.

large enough, so that in a given time an equal number of water molecules flow from solution to the pure water as are flowing in the reverse direction. In principle, water can be prevented from entering the solution across a semipermeable membrane in a simple osmometer (figure 2.5). This consists of a vessel containing pure water and a compartment containing a solution of concentration *c*, sealed at one end by a semipermeable membrane and at the other end by a frictionless piston; provided with a platform. The weight required on this platform just to prevent the entry of solvent through the membrane into the inner compartment is known as the *osmotic pressure*. It is therefore clear that a single, isolated solution does not have an osmotic pressure in the same sense as an isolated gas has a gas pressure. Osmotic pressure arises as a result of the tendency of water to move between two compartments in which the concentration of solutes is unequal. It might therefore be thought that ions dissolved in the soil solution are not a source of osmotic pressure, because osmotic pressure depends on the existence of compartments or regions of solution differing in concentration. Even if such differences arose temporarily in the soil solution (for instance, following fertilizer application), they would soon be dissipated by diffusion. However, plant roots in the soil solution can, as an approximation, be regarded as compartments isolated from the solution by membranes which are readily permeable to water but only a little permeable to ions. The observation that plants obtain water from a nonsaline solution more easily than from a saline one is the consequence of the osmotic forces just discussed.

As has been seen, osmotic pressure is a function of the concentration difference Δc between two compartments. The relation between osmotic pressure and concentration is known as *van't Hoff's law*

$$\Pi = RTc$$

where *R* is the gas constant and *T* is the absolute temperature. If the value of *R* is expressed as 0.082 litre atmosphere $mole^{-1} deg^{-1}$ and *c* in mole $litre^{-1}$, the osmotic pressure will be obtained in atmospheres. van't Hoff's law, like the ideal gas law to which it is analogous, holds good only at low solute concentration: deviations from the law are not serious for solutions of nonelectrolytes, but for ions (which represent the commonest solutes in soil solutions) the deviations do become important at concentrations occurring naturally. Under these conditions a corrected concentration (the *activity*) takes the place of concentration in the van't Hoff equation.

Not all ionic solutes are freely diffusible in the soil solution. In the neighbourhood of charged surfaces, ions bearing a charge which is opposite in sign to that of the surface are accumulated and their motion is restricted due to the electrostatic attraction between the surface and the ions. Thus a mechanism exists in soils, even in the absence of all types of membranes, giving rise to regions of solution which are equally accessible to water molecules but at different ion concentrations. When these counterions are

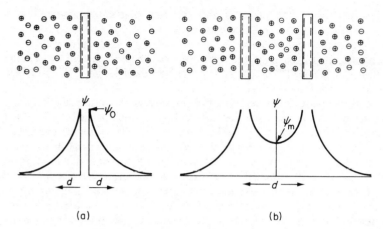

Figure 2.6 Electrical double layers at clay-particle surfaces in an electrolyte solution
(a) Noninteracting double layers. The electrical potential (ψ) has the value ψ_0 at the clay particle surface where $d = O$ (d is the distance measured from the particle surface). Counterions accumulate near the surface. The electrical potential falls off to O at long distances where the number of positive and negative charges in the solution are equal.
(b) Interacting double layers. The electrical potential midway between the platelets is ψ_m. The repulsion between the platelets depends on this midway potential.

located at the surface of a single charged clay particle, forming a so-called *noninteracting electrical double layer* (figure 2.6a), no net force acts on the water because the double layer system is in mechanical and electrostatic equilibrium. But when, as is usual in soils, two charged flat clay particles face each other to form what is known as an *interacting electrical double layer system* (figure 2.6b), the osmotic pressure due to the double layers tends to drive the clay platelets apart. This pressure is usually balanced by external mechanical or hydrostatic pressure on the clay platelets. The osmotic pressure Π, can be shown to be related to the electrical potential ψ_m midway between the clay particles and to the concentration of ions in the bulk solution c

$$\Pi = 2RTc \left(\cosh \frac{v e \psi_m}{kT} - 1 \right)$$

Here, v is the valency of the counterions, e is the electronic charge, and 'cosh' is a so-called hyperbolic function similar to the familiar trigonometric functions like cosine, values of which can be looked up in tables. Perusal of such tables shows that cosh $0 = 1$; it follows therefore that the osmotic pressure forcing two charged clay platelets apart disappears only when $\psi_m = 0$ (that is, when the electrical potential midway between the plates is zero and the plates are separated by a considerable distance on a molecular scale). These considerations also show that the repulsion between clay platelets is not simply electrostatic in nature, as it is between the plates of a condenser separated by vacuum, but electrochemical. The charges on the clay particles are largely shielded by the counterions at the clay surface.

A third mode for water retention in soils is the adsorption of water molecules onto the surfaces of colloidal soil particles and their coordination around the adsorbed ions, the so-called *water of hydration*. The forces involved are either of the universal London- van der Waals type, or hydrogen bonds. These are all short range forces and the adsorbed layers are generally thought to be restricted to a very few molecular layers in thickness. As has already been mentioned, the existence at surfaces of ordered water layers several tens of molecular layers thick has also been claimed. The question regarding the distance to which ordering of water molecules at surfaces extends is thus still open and further work is required to clarify it.

2.2 THE FREE ENERGY OF SOIL WATER

As a result of the existence of the forces of interaction between soil and water the transfer of unit quantity of water from an unsaturated soil into a large reservoir of pure and free water at the same temperature and elevation as the soil water requires the performance of work; this work is, in principle, a measure of the specific free energy of soil water or the *soil water potential*. The individual components of this free energy corresponding to the different forces just discussed are difficult to measure separately. In practice, only two components of the soil water potential can be distinguished experimentally: the *matric potential* or matric suction, which arises due to forces connected with the presence of the soil solid phase (the soil matrix), and the *solute potential* or solute suction, related to the presence of solutes in the soil solution. Fortunately such discrimination is sufficient for practical purposes. The soil water potential is the sum of the matric and solute potentials. These two components of the soil water potential can be measured separately or together in several ways. The principles of the most important methods will be discussed later in this chapter. First, however, it will be convenient to examine the different ways in which the soil water potential can be expressed. It is important to understand the relationship between terms like soil water potential, tension, suction and pF, because they are directly related — can be derived from each other — and are ultimately equivalent. This becomes apparent on examination of table 2.1. In column 1 of the table, the soil water potential is expressed in terms of energy per unit mass or (using cgs units) in erg gram^{-1}. This way of expressing the potential is closest to the fundamental definition of the specific free energy of water, but because

Table 2.1

Soil moisture tension scales †

1	2	3	4	5	6	7
Tension equivalent to					Suitable methods for tension measurement	
erg g^{-1}	Atmospheres (approx)	cm of water	pF	Relative humidity (per cent) at 25°C	On laboratory samples	in situ
9·81 x 10^9	10000	10^7	7			
				10		
9·81 x 10^8	1000	10^6	6	50		
				75		
9·81 x 10^7	100	10^5	5	93		
				98		
9·81 x 10^6	10	10^4	P.W.P.§ 4	99		
9·81 x 10^5	1	10^3	3	99·9		
			F.C.‡			
9·81 x 10^4	0·1	10^2	2			
9·81 x 10^3	0·01	10^1	1			
9·81 x 10^2	0·001	10^0	0			

Methods in column 6 (On laboratory samples): Vapour pressure; Pressure membrane; Tension plate. Methods in column 7 (in situ): Resistance blocks; Tensiometers.

† See reference 3 for this chapter.
‡ FC: the tension of soil water in soils at a moisture content corresponding to field capacity is usually in this range.
§ PWP: the tension of soil water in soils at a moisture content corresponding to the permanent wilting percentage is usually in this range.

the measurement of the work required to move unit mass of water from the soil solution into a large reservoir of free water is not easy to perform, the potential is rarely expressed in these units. For a fully saturated soil, the soil water potential would be zero erg per gram; this cannot be shown in table 2.1 which is on a logarithmic scale. At lower moisture contents, the soil water potential increases to very high values.

An alternative way of expressing the soil water potential is in terms of energy per unit volume of water, which has the same dimensions as pressure (table 2.1, column 2). The c.g.s. units are dyne cm^{-2}; larger, practical units are the bar (10^6 dyne cm^{-2}) and the atmosphere (1.01×10^6 dyne cm^{-2}). In an unsaturated soil, soil water pressure is negative; negative pressure is often referred to as suction or tension. In a saturated soil the pressure is either zero or positive, but this situation is not shown in table 2.1. The figures in column 2 of the table are given in atmospheres and can be derived from those in column 1 by multiplying with the density of water ($1 \, g \, cm^{-3}$) and by the numerical factor 9.87×10^{-7}, to convert erg cm^{-3} or dyne cm^{-2} into atmospheres. Pressure units are often used for expressing the values of the soil water potential: as will be seen later, pressure can be used directly in some methods of measuring the soil water potential or adjusting it to a predetermined level.

A third way of expressing the soil water potential is in terms of energy per unit weight which is equivalent to a hydraulic head (table 2.1, column 3); the c.g.s. units are cm H_2O. The hydraulic head equivalent to a given pressure is the height of the water column producing that pressure; for instance, the hydraulic head equivalent to 1 atmosphere is 1013 cm H_2O. Numerically the hydraulic head can also be derived from the values in column 1 by dividing with the gravitational constant, 981 cm s^{-2}.

The idea of the length of a water column suspended from a soil sample to represent the energy by which soil water is held is a simple one. The numerical values, however, cover a wide range from 0 cm at saturation to well over 10 000 cm in the moisture range of interest in the field. It has, therefore, become common practice to quote the logarithm of the height of the water column in cm, the so-called pF value (table 2.1, column 4) rather than the height itself. The pF scale is a convenient one ranging from 0.00 at saturation to about 7.00 for a soil dried at a temperature just over 100°C, covering the whole soil-moisture spectrum. The term pF was adopted by analogy with the pH scale convention: the logarithmic pH scale simplifies the handling of inconveniently small numbers, whereas the pF scale serves the same purpose for large ones.

Another phenomenon which can also be used to express the free energy level of soil water is the lowering of the vapour pressure (table 2.1, column 5). If the vapour pressure of free water at a given temperature is p_0, then the vapour pressure of water in equilibrium with a saturated, nonsaline soil will also be p_0 at the same temperature. If now some water is removed from the soil, leaving the remaining soil water under tension, the vapour pressure p of this remaining soil water will be lower than p_0. The relative humidity maintained in the atmosphere in equilibrium with the unsaturated soil is then $(p/p_0) \times 100$; this relative humidity is another measure of the soil water tension. Relative humidity is a dimensionless number; it is related to other soil moisture properties by the relationship $Mgh = 2.3RT\log(p/p_0)$, where M is the molecular weight of water, g the gravitational constant, h is the hydraulic head, R the molar gas constant and T the absolute temperature. Using this relationship and the numerical value of 8.3×10^7 erg degree^{-1} for R, the hydraulic head values in table 2.1 can be readily converted into relative humidity figures (table 2.1, column 5). If the soil is saline, then the moisture potential calculated from the vapour pressure in equilibrium with the soil will also include the osmotic contribution of the dissolved salts.

2.3 THE SOIL MOISTURE CHARACTERISTIC CURVE AND SOIL MOISTURE 'CONSTANTS'

It is obvious from the discussion so far that soil water tension is related to soil moisture content: the tension increases continuously with decreasing soil moisture content. Curves representing soil moisture content as a function of tension are known as *soil moisture* characteristic curves, or *soil moisture characteristics*. The moisture characteristics of soils with different textures are shown schematically in figure 2.7. At saturation, all

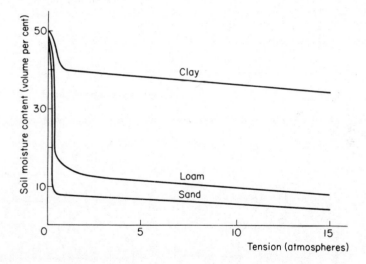

Figure 2.7   Typical soil-moisture characteristics for soils of different textures.

three soils have approximately the same moisture content. The curves have the same general shape: an initial rapid drop in moisture content in the lower than one atmosphere tension range is followed by a much slower decrease for all three soils. The moisture content of soils at all tensions decreases in the order clay > loam > sand. A clay soil may contain several times the quantity of moisture by volume than a sandy soil under the same tension. Another feature of these moisture characteristics is the slope of the curves between 1 and 15 atmospheres: the slope decreases in the order loam $\geqslant$ clay $>$ sand. This has some significance in connection with what may be called 'available' soil water, which will be discussed later.

When obtaining data for moisture-characteristic curves it should be remembered that a given soil has no unique moisture characteristic. The curves obtained differ depending on whether the soil under investigation is being wetted or dried. Such irreversible behaviour is known as *hysteresis* (figure 2.8). Along the *drying* or *moisture release curves*, the moisture

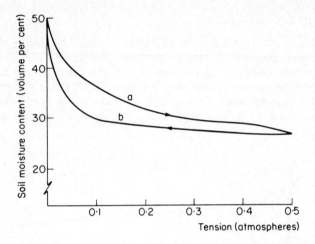

Figure 2.8 Hysteresis in the soil-moisture characteristic: (a) drying curve; (b) wetting curve.

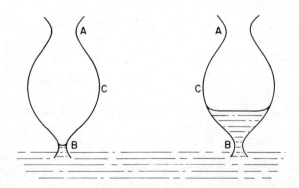

Figure 2.9′ Explanation of hysteresis in nonshrinking soils. The pore shown will empty at tensions corresponding to radius r_2 at B but will refill completely only if the tension is relaxed to a value corresponding to r_3 at C.

contents for any tension are usually higher than those corresponding to the same tension on the wetting or moisture retention curves. In nonswelling soils the hysteresis effect can be explained by considering that the soil pore space does not consist of pores of uniformly varying cross-section but of irregular interconnected cavities (figure 2.9). If suction is imposed on the soil from below, the large pore will empty only after the suction has exceeded the value required by the capillary pressure equation

$$P = 2\gamma/r_1$$

where r_1 is the radius of the narrow entry to the pore at A. The pore will then empty completely and the air—water interface will stabilize again at another point, say at B, where the pore radius r_2 is smaller than r_1. If it is now desired to let the pore refill with water, the tension must be relaxed until the capillary force is reduced to a value corresponding to $P = 2\gamma/r_3$ where r_3 is the largest radius of the pore at C. Then, but only then, will the rest of the pore fill completely. This explains the usually observed hysteresis in the moisture characteristics of nonswelling soils. In swelling clayey soils another mechanism is usually invoked to account for the hysteresis: this is the partial, irreversible rearrangement of the clay particles on drying, so that the rewetted soil will have a lower volume than the original sample.

It has been recognized for some time that the 'availability' of soil water to plants is related to the soil water tension and there has been a preference for expressing soil moisture parameters in terms of an equilibrium tension or suction, rather than in terms of soil moisture content. As has already been indicated, there is no discontinuity in the moisture characteristic curves and thus the designation of any particular values of moisture tension as soil moisture 'constants' is rather arbitrary. For practical purposes, however, particularly in connection with irrigation, it is useful to designate some limiting tension values. Provided that the arbitrary nature of the choice and the resulting lack of general applicability of the selected values is understood, the use of such limiting values is justified.

It has been a matter of observation for some time that drainage in the field slows down considerably a short time after rain or irrigation has ceased. It has even been claimed, incorrectly, that it stops entirely. This phenomenon is of considerable importance since the initial rapid drainage restores good aeration to part of the pore space while water retained in the other part is stored for use by plants during dry periods. Attempts were therefore made to define the moisture tension at what has become known as 'field capacity'. According to one definition, field capacity is 'the amount of water held in soil after excess water has drained away and the rate of downward movement has materially decreased, which takes place within two to three days after rain or irrigation in pervious soils of a uniform structure and texture'. This definition is rather vague but it does suggest a method whereby the approximate field capacity of a soil can be determined. The name itself implies a property of a soil in the field and this is where it is best measured. The soil should be wetted to a known depth, surface evaporation prevented and the moisture content at a fixed depth measured over a period of several weeks, at first frequently and then at progressively increasing intervals. If the moisture contents are then plotted against time, with time as the independent variable on the horizontal axis, the intersection of the straight lines resulting from the forward extrapolation of the initial steep part of the curve and from the backward extrapolation of the final flat part of the curve gives the approximate moisture content at which downward movement has 'materially decreased'.

Values of the field capacity vary from about 5 per cent by weight in sandy soils to about 50 per cent in clays; in peats the figure can exceed 100 per cent. The value is lower but is attained earlier and is more distinct in sandy soils than in clayey or organic ones. The nature of the clay material is also important: expanding clays like montmorillonite give rise to higher and less distinct field capacities than nonexpanding types of clay. The presence of impervious layers in the soil profile also affects redistribution and results in a higher apparent field capacity. When estimating the field capacity it is always assumed that the soil has been wetted to saturation to a depth greater than that at which the field capacity is to be measured. It is also assumed that water loss by means other than internal drainage (for instance, by surface evaporation or *evapotranspiration*) has been prevented.

When, the importance of energetics in soil–plant–water relationships was recognized, it was attempted to assign a unique moisture tension value to all soils at field capacity. Values such as 0.5 atmosphere (equivalent to pF 2.7) have been suggested. Such assignments have the advantage that the field capacity, or some figure related to it, becomes easily measurable in the field or even in the laboratory. No doubt such considerations have encouraged the adoption of ideas of this kind. They imply, however, that the field capacity is an equipotential equilibrium value, depending on the energy with which water is held in the soil; it is in fact a dynamic characteristic depending on soil moisture tension only indirectly; it depends more on the resistance offered by the soil to the movement of water. This resistance increases strongly when the water column in the soil profile breaks and becomes discontinuous. In principle, this should not occur before the tension reaches the value of about one atmosphere. In practice, however, the column breaks at tensions much lower than this, sandy soils requiring lower tensions than clay soils. Thus field capacity is not an equipotential soil constant in the sense that a unique pF value cannot be assigned to the field capacity in all soils; but it usually falls in the range between 0.1 to 0.5 atmospheres, or pF 2.0–2.7. Equipotential values, like the 1/3 bar (1 bar ≈ 1 atmosphere) percentage have been proposed from time to time. The estimation of moisture contents corresponding to such values is conveniently simple but the meaning of the results is less certain.

The field capacity, or the moisture content at some related moisture tension value, marks the upper limit of soil water content which plants can depend on in the field for longer periods of time. To serve as the lower limit, below which the major biological functions of plants are impeded, the *permanent wilting percentage* or permanent wilting point has been proposed. This has been defined as 'the moisture content in the root zone at which the wilted plant can no longer recover turgidity, even when it is placed in a saturated atmosphere for 12 hours'. A tension of 13.6 or 15 atmospheres has been assigned to the permanent wilting point by several workers; it is probably more realistic to assign it somewhere in the range of 10 to 25 atmospheres. This is a wide range of tensions but the corresponding changes in moisture content are rather small at these high tensions. The permanent wilting percentage is clearly not an equipotential soil moisture 'constant'. In the experimental determination of the wilting point, atttention should be given to the rate at which the soil water tension is lowered. This lowering should be slow enough to allow the root-water potential to come to equilibrium with the soil water potential. Evaporative demand (that is, the relative humidity in the atmosphere) should be controlled throughout the experiment. There are also difficulties in maintaining the soil at a uniform moisture tension throughout; the tension values are measured in the bulk soil sample, whereas the tension near the root surface is likely to be different and increasing as the root surface is approached.

Modern views tend to place less emphasis on the static picture of 'available soil water' as measured by the difference between the amounts stored by the soil between field capacity and permanent wilting point. It is now recognized that the supply of water to plants is a dynamic process, in which water is constantly transferred from the soil via the roots and leaves of plants to the atmosphere. The central part of this process, *transpiration*, depends on the morphological and physiological characteristics of the plant and can be controlled by either atmospheric or by soil conditions. In wet soils transpiration is controlled by the rate at which the atmosphere can draw water from the plant. In dry soils the ability of the soil to supply water to the roots sufficiently fast to keep up with the rate of evaporation by the plant would limit plant performance. Characterizing soil moisture by the static 'available soil water' principle is therefore a somewhat crude, although useful, approximation, the limitations of which are now being better understood. More attention is now given to the dynamic aspects of soil water relationships, which are discussed in the following section on soil water movement.

Occasionally soil moisture has been classified into *hygroscopic water*, *capillary water* and *gravitational water*. This nomenclature implies that soil moisture can somehow be fractionated. There is, however, no way to distinguish one water molecule from any other in soil water at equilibrium. Terms like the ones quoted are misleading and their use should therefore be discouraged.

2.4   THE FLOW OF SOIL WATER

Soil moisture is in a condition of complete equilibrium only if the forces acting on it are fully balanced. In the field this condition is rarely satisfied for any prolonged period. Soil water is therefore subject to movement, obvious examples of which are *infiltration* during rainfall or irrigation, or the removal of excess water by *drainage*. It is therefore necessary to consider the factors determining the rates of flow of water in soils.

Equations of flow relate the flow rate to the driving force on the fluid and to the resistance offered to flow by the fluid itself and by the medium containing the fluid. The most general expression relating the rates of flow to the viscosity of the fluid and to the driving force (the *potential gradient*) is the *Navier–Stokes law* for the isothermal flow of noncompressible fluids. The Stokes–Navier equations simplify considerably if the channels conducting the flow are small and the flow rate correspondingly is low; this is fortunately the case for the flow of water in soils. We shall here be concerned with only two special cases of the Stokes–Navier law: the flow of water in a capillary (*Poiseuille's equation*) and the flow of water in a porous medium (*Darcy's equation*).

One of the simplest types of conducting channel for water is a capillary tube of uniform cross-section with radius r, for which the flow rate is

$$q = \frac{r^4 \pi \Delta P}{8 \eta L}$$

where ΔP is the pressure difference, η the viscosity of the water and L the length of the capillary. This expression is known as Poiseuille's equation. If r and L are expressed in cm, ΔP in dyne cm^{-2} η in dyne s cm^{-2} (or poise, after Poiseuille), then the flow rate is obtained in cm^3 s^{-1}. In deriving this equation it has been assumed that when water moves through a capillary in response to a pressure difference, the water adheres to the wall of the capillary so that the velocity of flow at the wall is zero. The water velocity increases in adjacent, cylindrical layers (known as *laminae*) and reaches a maximum in the centre of the tube. Such flow is known as *laminar flow* to distinguish it from *turbulent flow*, where the flow rate is no longer proportional to the driving force (here, the pressure difference). The numerical constants in the equation are related to the circular shape of the cross-section of the capillary. Poiseuille's equation is applicable to laminar flow only and serves to emphasize the strong dependence of the flow rate on the radius of the conducting channel. If the flow rate through the capillary is expressed as the mean velocity of flow along the tube, the Poiseuille equation becomes

$$q/r^2\pi = \bar{q} = r^2 \Delta P/8\eta L$$

This form of the equation is useful for comparison with the Darcy equation and shows the similarities and differences between the factors controlling the flow rate in simple capillaries and in porous media like soils.

The relationship between the rate of flow of water in saturated beds of sand and the driving force was investigated by Darcy over a hundred years ago. He studied a system similar to that shown schematically in figure 2.10. The apparatus consists of a soil column of length L. The height of

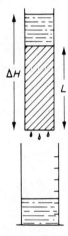

Figure 2.10   Darcy's apparatus for the study of the flow of water in saturated soils. During a flux measurement the level of water in the apparatus is kept constant by continuous supply of water.

the water level above that of the water outlet, ΔH, is known as the total pressure head or *hydraulic head*. Darcy found that in a saturated bed of sand the flux, or volume of water flowing through unit cross-section in unit time, was proportional to the hydraulic head per unit length of column

$$q \propto \frac{\Delta H}{L}$$

The flux is therefore proportional to the driving force just as it is in capillary flow. The constant of proportionality is known as the *hydraulic conductivity*, K. Darcy's equation can therefore be written

$$q = V/At = K\Delta H/L$$

where q is the flux, A the cross-sectional area of the column, and t the time. As the driving force term $\Delta H/L$ is dimensionless, the hydraulic conductivity has the same dimensions as the flux (that is, cm s^{-1}). The pore geometry in a porous medium such as soil is much more complicated than that of an assembly of capillary tubes. It is therefore not possible in Darcy's equation to express the hydraulic conductivity of the medium directly in terms of the pore radii and the viscosity of the liquid as for capillary flow. In Darcy's equation, therefore, the hydraulic conductivity K takes the place of the $r^2/8\eta$ term in the capillary flow equation. The hydraulic conductivity, as would be expected, depends on the properties of both the porous medium and of the flowing liquid. In principle it is possible to separate the hydraulic conductivity into two components, the *intrinsic permeability of the porous medium, k,* and the *viscosity of the liquid, η*

$$K = \frac{k}{\eta}$$

Such separation is, however, meaningful only for systems where the fluid and the porous medium do not interact, so that significant changes in the viscosity of the liquid can be introduced without affecting the pore structure (and thus the intrinsic permeability) of the solid. This is feasible in pure sands, but natural soils always contain sufficient colloidal material to make the distinction between the two components of the hydraulic conductivity impractical.

The hydraulic conductivity (or, strictly, the intrinsic permeability) is related to the pore geometry of the soil, but this geometry is so complicated that no general way has yet been devised for expressing intrinsic permeability in terms of some property of the soil pores or the pore size distribution which would be valid for all porous media. Progress, however, has been made in this field with nonshrinking, sandy materials. The hydraulic conductivity is therefore an empirically measured quantity; its magnitude is usually of the order of $10^{-2} - 10^{-3}$ cm s^{-1} for sands and can be as low as 10^{-7} cm s^{-1} for clays. The total porosity of clays usually exceeds that of sands and the hydraulic conductivity figures reflect the disproportionately large contribution to the conductivity of the wider pores in sands as compared with the narrow pores in clays. Under field conditions flow in large cracks, fissures and root channels can dominate the hydraulic conductivity of a clay soil in the saturated region and the conductivity may then even exceed that of sandy soils.

Darcy's equation implies that the hydraulic conductivity of a soil is constant: there are, however, limitations on the constancy of the hydraulic conductivity for soils in the field and even for strictly nonshrinking porous media such as sands. The hydraulic conductivity of a soil depends strongly on the state of flocculation of the soil and that in turn is affected by the type and concentration of the ions dissolved in the soil solution. For instance, the hydraulic conductivity of a soil reclaimed from the sea may be high initially, while the soil is in equilibrium with seawater which is approximately 0.5 molar with respect to sodium chloride. A tenfold reduction of this concentration brought about by leaching with rainwater can deflocculate the soil and mobilize some of the clay material blocking the conducting channels, thereby reducing the conductivity by one or more orders of magnitude. It is necessary under these conditions to maintain the state of flocculation of the soil by the addition of flocculating ions such as Ca^{2+} (usually in the form of $CaSO_4$). Gas bubbles, such as those of entrapped air or of carbon dioxide produced by microbial action, can also block conducting channels and change the apparent hydraulic conductivity of a soil.

The validity of Darcy's equation is limited to relatively low fluxes where the flow is laminar rather than turbulent. In turbulent flow, a unit increase in hydraulic head is less efficient in increasing the flux than in laminar flow, thus causing an apparent decrease in hydraulic conductivity at high flow rates. This limitation, which also applies to capillary flow, is fortunately not serious for soils where the flow of water under practical conditions is sufficiently slow to be regarded as laminar.

In the root zone of plants the soil is saturated usually only during and immediately after rain or irrigation; otherwise unsaturated conditions prevail. It is therefore of interest to consider the factors affecting the flow of water in unsaturated soils. As in saturated soils the flow is determined by the driving force and by the conductivity: the flux is the product of these two terms as before. One difference is that the driving force is now the gradient of a negative pressure (or suction) and not of a positive hydraulic head. Such suction gradients can be very large compared with the gradients produced by gravity, especially during infiltration of rain or irrigation water into dry soil. The corresponding fluxes would be very large indeed were it not for the relatively low hydraulic conductivities associated with unsaturated flow. The drop in unsaturated conductivity compared to that in saturated flow arises from the loss of effective conducting pores as more and more channels are drained under the increasing suction regimes. The reduction in conductivity with increasing suction is very rapid as large pores, which, as shown by Poiseuille's equation, are most effective in conducting water, are being drained first. The principles of saturated and unsaturated flow are therefore similar. The detailed quantitative treatment of unsaturated flow is more complicated because, although Darcy's equation can be generalized to cover unsaturated flow, the hydraulic conductivity is no longer constant but becomes a function of the soil water suction and this must be taken into account.

It would be expected that the unsaturated flux would be greater in sandy soils than in clay soils. This is usually confirmed by observation, provided that the soil is not far removed from saturation. At increasing suctions the conductivity of a sandy soil drops more rapidly than that of a clay soil and the flux is then often greater and continues for longer in the clay soil than in the sand. A sandy layer in the soil profile can even act as a barrier to unsaturated flow rather than enhance it: the passage of water from the narrow pores of the clay into the wide pores of the sand will only be possible when the clay soil becomes nearly saturated and the tension drops to a low value.

The main contribution to water movement in unsaturated soils is that of liquid flow. Soil air always contains water vapour, however, and some water movement therefore would be expected to take place through the vapour phase too. To obtain an estimate of the possible importance of this effect, it is necessary to examine the conditions affecting the water vapour movement in soils. Such movement is a result either of *mass flow* or of *diffusion*. Mass flow occurs in response to differences in total gas pressure; such differences are however unimportant in soil air. The diffusion flux, like the flux in saturated and unsaturated liquid flow, is again controlled by a driving force (in this case the vapour pressure gradient) and by a conductivity contribution (the diffusion coefficient for water vapour). The total flux is, as usual, the product of the two terms. Water movement by vapour diffusion will therefore be important only under conditions which allow the development of major differences in water vapour pressure over the soil profile. Such large differences do not arise in response to suction gradients: inspection of table 2.1 shows that the drop in relative humidity from saturation to the wilting point range at $25°C$ is only about 1 per cent. The vapour pressure of water is, however, rather sensitive to temperature: it increases by about 6 per cent per degree in the $10-25°C$ range. Water vapour would therefore tend to diffuse from the hotter to the colder regions of the soil; the diurnal pattern of movement would be downwards during the day and upwards at night. Vapour pressure differences could also arise due to differences in osmotic pressure of the soil solution in various regions of the soil profile; such differences are not important, however, except in saline soils.

2.5   INFILTRATION AND DRAINAGE

The process of entry of rain or irrigation water into the soil is known as *infiltration*. The rate of infiltration or *infiltrability* is an important property of a soil, because together with the supply rate it determines what proportion of the water supplied can penetrate the soil. As long as the infiltration rate exceeds the supply rate, all the water will enter the soil; the infiltration is then said to be *rain-intensity controlled*. If, however, the supply rate exceeds the infiltrability, then part of the supplied water will be stored on the surface and the rest will be lost as run-off. Infiltration is then said to be *profile controlled*. The infiltration rate is generally not constant with time, but varies in a manner depending on whether infiltration is rain-intensity controlled or profile controlled and also on the properties of the soil. When the rain intensity is low and constant (below the value of the saturated hydraulic conductivity), the soil will not become saturated and a steady infiltration rate will be reached corresponding to the unsaturated conductivity at the limiting suction maintained by the low rain intensity (figure 2.11a). If the rain intensity is

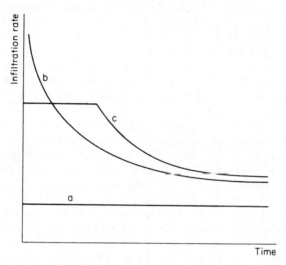

Figure 2.11 (a) Infiltration rate at low rain intensity; (b) infiltration rate at high rain intensity; (c) infiltration rate at intermediate rain intensity.

high enough to exceed not only the saturated hydraulic conductivity but also the initial infiltration rate (figure 2.11b), the surface will become flooded and the infiltration rate will decrease, eventually reaching a constant value known as the *final infiltration rate*. If the rain intensity is higher than the saturated hydraulic conductivity but lower than the initial infiltrability (figure 2.11c), then the infiltration rate remains rain-intensity controlled for some time; at a later stage, the rate of infiltration drops, the surface becomes flooded as the infiltration becomes profile controlled and eventually reaches the final infiltration rate. The decrease in infiltration rate with time is due to either a decrease in the driving force (that is, of the moisture potential gradient) as the soil is wetted, or to a decrease in the conductivity of the soil as the pore size distribution is altered by partial deflocculation and breaking down of soil crumbs during wetting. It would therefore be expected that the initial infiltration rate would be higher into a dry soil than into the same soil when wet. Similarly, initial infiltration would be faster into a soil having a porous top layer than into a similar one having a uniform pore size distribution. A surface crust reduces both the initial and the final infiltration rate. The value of the final infiltration rate is usually of the same order of magnitude as the saturated hydraulic conductivity; it may exceed 10^{-3} cm s^{-1} in sands and it is often less than 10^{-5} cm s^{-1} for clays.

Water that is unable to infiltrate the soil first accumulates in puddles on the surface. When these are filled to capacity, the excess constitutes *surface run-off*. Such run-off may cause *erosion* which is harmful. It is therefore desirable to keep the infiltration rate as high as possible by maintaining good soil-surface porosity and to prevent capping by cultivation, mulching or application of suitable soil conditioners.

Downward movement of water continues for some time after the stoppage of rain. This process is known as *redistribution* if the water table is far below the soil surface. The movement of water in the course of redistribution is caused mostly by suction gradients. The movement is more rapid initially, while these gradients are larger, and slows down with the dissipation of the gradient and with the decrease in the moisture content resulting in lower unsaturated conductivities in the water-conducting layers. In sandy soils redistribution slows down considerably after 2 or 3 days; this has led to the concept of field capacity for the moisture content retained by soils in the field, as has already been discussed. In clay soils redistribution may continue for weeks, because the unsaturated conductivity of clay soils decreases more slowly with moisture content than that of sands. The field capacity of clay soils is therefore less distinct than that of sands.

The movement of water in the soil profile in the presence of a water table near the soil surface is known as *internal drainage*. *Ground-water drainage* is the artificial control of the height of the water table by the removal of excess soil water. The need for ground-water drainage does not arise from a need to remove water itself from the plant root environment: it is well known that aqueous solutions can act as quite satisfactory growth media for plants as long as mechanical support for them is provided and the solution is adequately aerated. The drainage of waterlogged soils is made necessary by the low partial pressure of oxygen in such soils; if uncorrected, this leads to undesirable anaerobic processes such as denitrification, or the accumulation of toxic amounts of reduced ions of iron or manganese. Low oxygen pressure also inhibits root respiration; cultivation of wet soils damages the soil structure. Drainage may be necessary, however, not only on waterlogged soils but also as a part of irrigation schemes. Unless the water table is kept deep enough, the capillary rise of water brings salts into the surface layers; evaporation leads to salt accumulation in the root zone, eventually rendering the soil unfit for supporting plant growth.

In ground-water drainage the soil is always saturated; in other words, soil water is always under positive hydrostatic pressure, not under suction. The effective conductivity is the saturated hydraulic conductivity which does not alter much in the course of drainage. Problems of flow during drainage would therefore appear to be somewhat simpler than those of unsaturated flow. Complications arise, however, from the variations of the hydraulic conductivity and of the hydrostatic pressure in space: these variations are due to heterogeneity in the soil profile, and to the resulting unevenness of the depth of the water table.

One of the usual problems in the design of drainage systems is the choice of a suitable *drain depth* and *spacing* to ensure that the water table remains below a required level. One of the approximate solutions to this problem is *Hooghoudt's equation*

$$S^2 = \frac{4KH}{q}(2d+H)$$

where S is the drain spacing, K the saturated hydraulic conductivity, q the rain intensity, H the maximum height of the water table above the drains and d is the height of the drains above an impermeable layer. To obtain a drain spacing, the variables on the right-hand side must be estimated or selected. In spite of the crudeness of the assumptions applied in arriving at the constant values for the quantities required for estimation of drain spacing, Hooghoudt's equation usually gives satisfactory results and is widely used.

2.6 SOIL WATER MEASUREMENTS: AMOUNTS AND TENSIONS

It is often required for practical purposes to obtain an estimate of the moisture content or the tension of water in a soil. The principles of the methods in common use will now be discussed. The amount of water in an unsaturated soil and the tension under which it is held are related. A tension measurement on a particular soil is sometimes calibrated in terms of moisture content and vice versa. However, the relationship between moisture content and tension is not unique because of hysteresis, as has already been discussed. The appropriate moisture characteristic for applications involving continuous reduction in the moisture content of soils (for instance, loss through plant uptake, evaporation or drainage) is the *moisture release* or *desorption curve*, whereas the *moisture retention* or *sorption curve* is appropriate for use with processes involving water gain, such as infiltration. Conductivity measurements are most frequently required on saturated soils in connexion with drainage and irrigation; the unsaturated hydraulic conductivity of a soil can also be measured. Hydraulic conductivity measurements will not be considered here.

The simplest method for measuring the moisture content of a soil sample is to weigh, dry and reweigh it. The ambiguities of this procedure arise from the difficulties in taking representative samples of convenient size, and from the different patterns of weight loss of soil materials on heating. The usual procedure is to heat the sample to 105°C for 24 hours; some soil clays retain adsorbed water at this temperature while labile organic matter may simultaneously be lost from some soils. The process is also laborious and time consuming; continuous sampling from the same location is also difficult.

A recently developed field method for the measurement of the moisture content of soils *in situ* is based on the ability of the nuclei of hydrogen atoms to slow down fast neutrons on collision. If a soil material is bombarded with fast neutrons, these will be in collision with the nuclei of all the atoms present; the loss of velocity of the neutrons will be greater on collision with the smallest nuclei — those of the hydrogen atoms. The number of slow neutrons produced in a soil when it is exposed to a standard source of fast neutrons is therefore directly related to the hydrogen content of the soil. Hydrogen occurs in soils either as part of water or as a component of organic molecules: the organic hydrogen can usually be regarded as constant and is also negligible compared with the hydrogen in water in all except peat soils. The probe of the neutron moisture meter consists of a source of fast neutrons, and a detector of slow neutrons. The flux of these slow neutrons is monitored and is a measure of the moisture content of the soil. The slow neutrons form a spherical cloud around the probe, the density of the cloud being highest near the probe and falling off with distance. In a wet soil the slow neutrons will be concentrated near the probe; in dry soils the slow neutrons will diffuse further away in the soil. Thus the volume of soil over which the neutron cloud is spread is smaller for wet soils than for dry ones. The flux of slow neutrons at the probe is calibrated in terms of moisture content by independent methods.

The moisture content of soils may also be measured by indirect techniques such as tensiometers or resistance blocks. These devices, however, respond to soil moisture tension rather than to moisture content as such; they will be discussed in the following sections.

Soil moisture tension can be estimated in many different ways; each method is appropriate for a particular tension range. Some methods measure the matric suction only, others respond to the total suction; the osmotic contribution to the total suction, due to freely diffusing solutes, can also be measured separately. The contributions of the matric and osmotic components to the total suction are shown schematically in the isothermal equilibrium membrane system (figure 2.12). The compartment containing the wet soil is open to the atmosphere and is in contact both with pure water through a membrane permeable to water only and with soil solution by a membrane permeable to water and solutes. The manometer on the right, in contact with pure water, registers the total suction, while the manometer in the centre, in contact with the soil solution, shows the matric suction only. The difference between the two is the solute suction. This can also be registered directly by the differential manometer on the left, connected to the soil solution compartment and to a compartment containing pure water; these two compartments are in

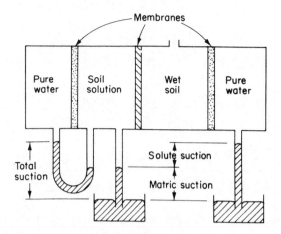

Figure 2.12 Isothermal membrane system at equilibrium

The membrane in the centre is permeable to solutes and to water; the membranes on either side are permeable to water only. (Black, 1965, Volume 1, p.130).

contact through a membrane permeable to water molecules only. Membranes permeable to water and to solutes are available in practice and are used to measure the soil matric suction. Practical membranes which are permeable to water only are not available, but soil water can be allowed to come to equilibrium with water in another compartment through the vapour phase. The vapour is 'permeable' to water but not to solutes. Solute suction is equivalent to the osmotic pressure of the soil solution and is thus also subject to independent measurement.

Soil water itself is not directly accessible for tension measurement. In general, therefore, an external body of water is allowed to come to equilibrium with the soil water and the tension of this external water, which by definition is equal to the soil water tension, is then measured. One common device for this purpose is the *tension plate* for use with soil samples in the laboratory and its equivalent for *in situ* measurements in the field or in the greenhouse, the *tensiometer*.

In the tension plate assembly, the contact between the water in the soil and the external water is maintained through a porous plate, which is usually built into the floor of a funnel (figure 2.13). The funnel is connected to a burette by either flexible or rigid tubing. The burette and the funnel are filled with water up to the porous plate. The soil sample is placed on the porous plate and is flooded with water by raising the burette with respect to the funnel if the coupling is flexible or by addition of water to the burette if the coupling is rigid. The level of water in the burette is then adjusted to that of the porous plate, and the soil is just saturated with water. Suction can be imposed on the water in the soil by

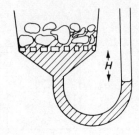

Figure 2.13   Tension-plate apparatus

The tension imposed on the soil water is equivalent to the hydraulic head *H*.
(See p.101 of reference 2 for this chapter).

lowering the level of water in the burette relative to the porous plate. The distance between the meniscus in the burette and the porous plate is the hydraulic head, while the volume of water withdrawn from the soil at the same time can be read off the burette. The limits of the range of use of the tension plate are determined by the size of pores in the plate and by the tensile strength of water columns in the apparatus. Air will not leak through the plate as long as the tension applied does not exceed the value determined by the largest pore in the plate. This would not seriously limit the range of applicability of the tension plate apparatus, as membranes with suitably small pores are now available. A more basic limitation is that when the hydraulic head reaches the equivalent of one atmosphere, the absolute hydrostatic pressure in the water at the porous plate approaches zero. Attempts to increase the head further would result in the absolute value of the hydrostatic pressure becoming negative and the water coming under tensile stress. Macroscopic water columns do not appear to possess tensile strength, so that a water column subjected to tensions in excess of atmospheric would fall away from the porous plate. The tension plate is therefore applicable to measurements of tensions between 0 and about 0.8 atmospheres only.

The principle of the tensiometer is the same as that of the tension plate but it is designed for *in situ* moisture tension measurements. The soil water is in contact with the water in the manometer through a porous pot which is buried in the soil at the required depth (figure 2.14) in such a way as to insure the best possible contact between the pot and the soil. The pot and the standpipe connecting it to the surface are filled with water; the end of the standpipe is connected to a mercury manometer or to a pressure gauge. When equilibrium between the soil water and the water in the tensiometer has been obtained, the pressure at the pot is $\rho_m g h_m - \rho_w g h_w$ and the equivalent hydraulic head is $\rho_m h_m - h_w$ centimetres of water. The porous materials used for the construction of the tension plate and the tensiometer are permeable to the solutes in the soil solution: the tension

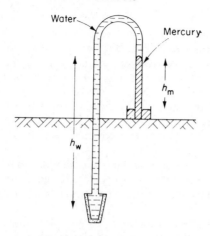

Figure 2.14   Schematic diagram of a tensiometer for use in the field
(See p.101 of reference 2 for this chapter).

measured by these instruments is therefore the matric suction. The use of
the tensiometer, like that of the tension plate, is limited to the 0–0.8
atmosphere tension range. Much of the water used by plants is, however,
drawn from soils containing water at these tensions. The tensiometer is a
useful practical instrument especially in the low tension range where data
are required for irrigation control.

The basic limitation restricting the use of tensiometers to below
tensions of one atmosphere can be overcome if, instead of *reducing* the
pressure of the external water in equilibrium with the soil solution with
respect to the air surrounding it (as is done on the tension plate), the air
pressure above the soil is *increased* relative to the external body of water
which is at atmospheric pressure. The device known as a *pressure plate* or
pressure-membrane apparatus depending on the construction of the porous
material used, consists of a chamber which can be put under elevated
pressure (figure 2.15). The floor of the chamber incorporates a porous

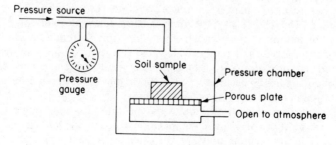

Figure 2.15. Schematic diagram of pressure-plate apparatus.

material: either a ceramic plate or a membrane. Ceramic plates can support pressures of the order of tens of atmospheres, whereas membranes withstand pressures greater than this by a factor of ten. The soil sample is placed into the chamber over the porous material and the chamber put under pressure: water drains out of an originally saturated soil into an external compartment which is at atmospheric pressure. At equilibrium the moisture in the soil will be subject to a tension equivalent to the difference between the pressure inside the chamber and outside it. The moisture content of the sample corresponding to this tension can then be determined. The pressure plate or pressure membrane is therefore not a direct method for measuring moisture tensions but of adjusting the moisture tension of soil samples to predetermined levels and measuring the corresponding moisture contents. The porous plate is again permeable to solutes so that the tension measured is the soil matric suction. A membrane, on the other hand, may retain at least some of the solutes in the soil solution. In the extreme case of a membrane permeable to water only, the pressure membrane apparatus would measure the sum of the matric and osmotic components of the soil moisture potential.

If a block of porous material is buried in a soil, the potential of water in the block at equilibrium will become equal to that in the soil with which it is in contact. The tension of water in the porous block, or its moisture content, can then be estimated by different methods; the commonest one is the measurement of the electrical conductivity between two electrodes permanently embedded into the porous block. For this measurement, the blocks need not be removed from the soil. The conductivity in the block depends not only on its moisture content, which itself depends on the moisture tension, but also on the concentration of solutes and on the temperature of the penetrating solution. Concentration effects can largely be overcome by constructing the block from gypsum; this salt is sufficiently soluble to keep the imbibed solution saturated with respect to its ions, thus suppressing the effect of other ions in the soil solution. Temperature effects can be corrected for. The gypsum blocks deteriorate after prolonged periods in the soil due to partial dissolution. Blocks made of porous fibre-glass or of nylon are not subject to such damage, but are very sensitive to changes in the electrolyte concentration of the soil solution. The choice of type of resistance block depends on the soil moisture tension range over which it is required to function: ideally the block should gain and release water gradually and continuously over the desired tension range. Porous blocks exhibit hysteresis and are not capable of producing highly accurate results; they function better in drier soils, in the tension range exceeding one atmosphere.

It is also possible to equilibrate the moisture in a soil sample with an external solution of known composition through the vapour phase. At equilibrium the vapour pressure of water in the soil and that over the external solution will be equal, water having distilled from a region of originally high to a region of originally low vapour pressure, from the soil into the external solution or vice versa. This principle can easily be used to adjust the moisture in a soil sample to a preselected tension. The soil sample is placed in an enclosure, usually into a vacuum desiccator, over a solution of known vapour pressure, usually the solution of a salt or of sulphuric acid. The volume of the solution must be large enough for its concentration to remain essentially unchanged on a loss or gain of water from the soil. The relative humidity of the chamber is now controlled by the solution present in excess. After equilibrium has been attained the soil samples, now at the preselected moisture tension corresponding to the relative humidity in the chamber, are removed and their moisture contents determined. The tension under which the water is held can be worked out from the relative humidity in the enclosure (see page 46). This method gives both the matric and the osmotic components of the soil water potential, since the vapour phase is permeable to water molecules but not to solutes. The range of applicability of the method is unfortunately limited to dry soils, at a tension above 15 atmospheres: this corresponds to a relative humidity not exceeding 99 per cent (see table 2.1). It is very difficult in practice to produce solutions maintaining relative humidities in the range of 99 to 100 per cent, corresponding to the moisture tension range of greatest interest for plants.

The contribution of solute suction to the soil water potential can be evaluated independently by measuring the concentration of solutes in the soil solution. The commonest method for doing this is the measurement of the electrical conductivity of a soil extract. Such measurements register the effect of ionic solutes only; since, however, ions represent the bulk of dissolved matter in soil solutions, the error in neglecting the other components is not serious. The contribution of solute suction to the moisture potential is important only in saline soils or in artificial growth media which have been allowed to accumulate salts through inadequate drainage. The sum of the solute and matric suctions should, in principle, add up to the soil moisture potential. This expectation has been confirmed by separate independent measurements of all three variables.

2.7   SOIL AERATION

The respiration of plant roots and of micro-organisms in soils depends on a constant supply of oxygen and results in the continuous release of carbon dioxide. Most terrestrial plants obtain the oxygen for root respiration from the soil, though some diffusion of oxygen within the plant can also occur. In the absence of movements of oxygen and of carbon dioxide into and out of the soil, these gases would accumulate resulting first in the inhibition of plant root activities and finally in the death of the roots. The process of exchange of oxygen and carbon dioxide between the soil air and the atmosphere is called *soil aeration*. Measurements indicate that the oxygen consumption of a square metre of soil is of the order of 10 litres per day, which corresponds to about 50 litres of air. Assuming an air-filled porosity of 20 per cent for the soil or 200 litres of air in a cubic metre of soil and uniform respiration to a depth of 1 metre, the daily oxygen consumption would amount to a quarter of the total amount of oxygen present. There are indications too that the bulk of the oxygen is used by soil micro-organisms rather than by plant roots. Micro-organisms could effectively compete with plant roots for oxygen, particularly at high soil moisture contents, because the number of micro-organisms is known to be higher in the rhizosphere than elsewhere in the soil.

The exchange of oxygen and of carbon dioxide between the soil and the atmosphere occurs partly in the air-filled pore space and partly through the pores filled with water. In the air-filled pore space, gases move either by mass flow or by diffusion. Mass flow of gases does occur to some extent as a result of temperature or pressure gradients, or due to increases in the volume of air filled pore space following the withdrawal of water but the importance of such mass flow is thought to be limited. The main process of redistribution of gases in the air-filled pore space is by diffusion. As with water vapour diffusion the diffusion rate again depends mainly on the effective porosity, rather than on the size distribution of the conducting pores.

Oxygen and carbon dioxide can also diffuse in the water-filled pore spaces; there are at least two reasons why these processes have until recently been relatively neglected. The solubility of oxygen in water is low: at room temperature and atmospheric pressure, the atmosphere contains 21 per cent by volume of oxygen and 0.03 per cent carbon dioxide, whereas water saturated with air contains only 0.6 per cent by volume of oxygen, but 2.25 per cent carbon dioxide. Also, the conductivity (or, strictly, the diffusion coefficient) of oxygen in the water filled pore space is lower by a factor of about 10^4 than it is in air-filled pores. On these grounds alone it may be thought that diffusion of oxygen through water in soils can be neglected from the plants' point of view. It is now realized, however, that the active plant root surface, like the surfaces of soil particles, is covered with water films of variable thickness; the final stages of diffusion of oxygen to, and carbon dioxide from the root surface necessarily occur through a water film. These diffusion steps may under certain conditions control the supply of oxygen to plant roots.

The characterization of the *aeration status* of soils involves considerations that are in some respects similar to those relating to the characterization of soil water. One aspect of aeration status is the quantity of air present in the soil, related to the air-filled pore space. Another aspect is the composition of the gas phase, represented by the partial pressures of the individual components, which are related to the energy status of the individual gases at the time of measurement. Yet another aspect of aeration status is the rate of diffusion of oxygen or of carbon dioxide, which are related to the ability of the soil to maintain an adequate supply of oxygen or an adequate rate of removal of carbon dioxide from the surface of plant roots.

The total volume of air-filled pore space in a soil required for adequate aeration has been found to vary between 5 and 15 per cent by volume. Below these levels the rate of diffusion of oxygen to the roots seems to limit adequate plant growth. Diffusion of gases proceeds at a finite rate and so the composition of soil air differs from that of the atmosphere. This composition is not uniform but depends on the rates of oxygen consumption and carbon dioxide production, and on the rates of diffusion at different depths in the profile. In aerobic respiration the volume of carbon dioxide produced is equal to the volume of oxygen used; the sum of the partial pressures of oxygen and of carbon dioxide are therefore the same in the soil as they are in the atmosphere. The average carbon dioxide content of soil air near the soil surface is about 0.3–1.0 per cent; it contains ten to thirty times more of this gas than does the atmosphere. There is a corresponding reduction in the average oxygen content of soil air, but as atmospheric air contains about 21 per cent oxygen, this reduction is relatively small. The carbon dioxide content of soil air usually increases and the oxygen content accordingly decreases with depth in the soil profile.

The main function of oxygen related to plant growth is that of an electron acceptor which may function, for instance, in the following way

$$O_2 + 4H^+ + 4e^- \rightleftharpoons 2 H_2O$$

Systems containing electron acceptors (oxidizing agents) and electron donors (reducing agents) are known as *oxidation–reduction* or *redox systems*. While the potential supplies of molecular oxygen and of water in aerated soils are unlimited, oxygen and its reduced form — water — are not the only redox couple present: oxidized and reduced forms of some metal ions, such as iron and manganese are other examples and in plant cells there are coordinated systems of electron donors and acceptors. It would therefore be reasonable to look for a soil property which would be a measure of not just the oxygen partial pressure but of the position of the oxidation–reduction equilibria established in all the redox systems of the soil. Such a property, at least in principle, is the *redox potential*; this can be measured (figure 2.16) as the potential difference between an inert platinum electrode and a reference electrode inserted into the soil, when the cell is adjusted so that no current flows in it. The arrangement shown in figure 2.16 is schematic only; in practice electronic instrumentation would have to be used to minimize current flow and hence a change in the balance of the soil redox systems while carrying out the measurement. In principle such measurements are no more complicated, and require much the same instrumentation, as pH measurements; yet, redox potentials are not measured routinely due to various difficulties. The potentials are often

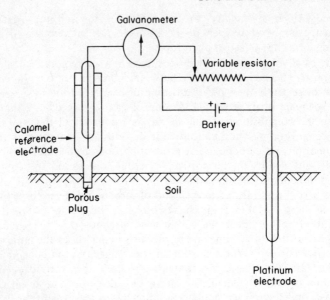

Figure 2.16 Schematic diagram of an apparatus for the measurement of the redox potential or of the rate of oxygen diffusion in soils
When measuring the redox potential, the variable resistance is set so that the voltage across the electrode system is exactly balanced (backed out) by the applied battery voltage. The voltage applied, corrected for by the known potential of the reference electrode, is the *redox potential*.
When measuring the rate of diffusion of oxygen, an external voltage in the range of $-0.4 - \sim 0.65$ volt is applied; the current registered on the galvanometer, corrected for the area of the platinum electrode, should be independent of the voltage applied; it is a measure of the rate of diffusion of oxygen to the electrode.

poorly reproducible due to the unstable nature of the redox equilibria in soils and also to the ease with which the platinum electrodes are poisoned. Some redox systems in soils are sluggish and come to equilibrium very slowly, if at all. The hydrogen ion concentration in the soil solution often affects the measured redox potential directly or indirectly: proper correction for the pH effect could only be made if the redox systems in operation were fully known, and such information is usually not available. The use of redox potentials is therefore restricted in practice to waterlogged soils in which the oxygen pressure or the oxygen diffusion rate are too low to be measured.

An electrode assembly similar to that shown in figure 2.16 can also be used to obtain a different characteristic of soil aeration: *oxygen diffusion rate* in the soil. In this application electrons are supplied to the platinum electrode not by the redox systems of the soil but from an external source, and the resulting current is measured, rather than being backed out, as in the measurement of the redox potential. If an electric potential of suitable magnitude is applied to a platinum electrode like that shown in figure 2.16, oxygen arriving at the electrode (cathode) surface will be reduced to water ($O_2 + 4H^+ + 4e^- \rightleftharpoons 2 H_2O$) or to hydroxyl ions ($O_2 + 2H_2O + 4e^- \rightleftharpoons 4 OH^-$) Either reaction results in the transport of four electrons for each molecule of oxygen reduced at the electrode. If it is assumed that the reaction rate is controlled not by the electrode process but by the rate of diffusion of oxygen to the electrode, the resulting current per unit area of electrode surface can be used as a measure of the oxygen diffusion rate. The results are fairly simple to interpret if the current remains constant over a wide range of applied voltages, as is found to be the case in soils saturated with water. The voltage applied to the platinum electrode is usually in the range of -0.40 to -0.65 volt; the former value is preferable in acid soils, to minimize the undesirable side reaction of H^+ ion reduction. In unsaturated soils the current appears to increase continuously with applied voltage, and the interpretation and the comparison of results obtained with different soils becomes complicated because many factors affect them which are not easy to control and which do not affect measurements in saturated soils.

An aspect of the different aeration measurements in relation to plant growth is the problem of integration of the aeration properties over longer periods of time. There are indications that plant performance may be limited more by short periods of stress due to oxygen deficiency than by average values calculated over longer periods.

SUMMARY

The main molecular components of the plant root environment are the soil water and the gases in the soil air filling the pore space. Proper functioning of roots depends on an adequate rate of supply of both water and oxygen. This rate depends on the geometrical properties of the pore space and on the electrochemical properties of the soil particle surfaces.

The forces of water retention in soils are the surface tension at the curved air—water interfaces in the soil pores (capillarity), the osmotic forces due to the presence of exchangeable ions and short-range forces of hydration associated with soil particle surfaces. As a result of these forces withdrawal of water from an unsaturated soil requires the expenditure of work. A quantitative expression of this work is the specific free energy of soil water, also known as the soil water potential or soil water tension. The soil water tension increases with decreasing soil moisture content.

Soil water tension can be expressed in terms of energy per unit mass, or energy per unit volume or energy per unit weight. In practice an often used scale is the pF scale, which is the logarithm of the soil water tension expressed in terms of energy per unit weight, or hydraulic head.

The curves relating the soil water tension to the amount of water in the soil are known as soil moisture characteristic curves. There is no unique moisture characteristic curve for any given soil; the curves are subject to hysteresis.

Attempts have been made to assign unique moisture potentials to soils with moisture contents corresponding to field capacity and to permanent wilting point. However, the operational definitions of field capacity and wilting point involve properties related to water movement and so static properties like the soil water tension can only approximately, even if conveniently, define the field capacity or the permanent wilting point.

The flow of water in capillaries is described by Poiseuille's equation. For porous media like soils, Darcy's equation applies, relating the flow rate to the driving force and to the hydraulic conductivity of the soil. Darcy's equation is valid for flow in both saturated and unsaturated soils: in the latter, the hydraulic conductivity is not constant but depends on the soil water tension.

The bulk of soil water movement takes place in pores filled with liquid water, but a small part may also occur in the vapour phase in response to temperature gradients.

Infiltration is the process whereby rain or irrigation water enters the soil; this is a process of unsaturated or of saturated flow depending on the relative magnitude of the rain intensity and the rate of infiltration. Drainage is the movement of water in the soil profile in the presence of a water table near the surface, and the control of the height of the water table by the removal of excess soil water. It usually involves saturated flow.

A range of methods is available for the estimation of moisture contents and moisture tensions both in the laboratory and in the field. Moisture contents can be measured by drying and weighing of samples in the laboratory or by the neutron moisture meter *in situ* in the field. Soil moisture tensions are measured with the tension plate, the pressure-membrane apparatus or by the vapour pressure method in the laboratory. In the field tensiometers and electrical resistance blocks are available; each technique covers a certain range of tensions.

Soil aeration is the exchange of oxygen and carbon dioxide between the soil air and the atmosphere. The exchange is the result of mass flow of gases and, more important, of diffusion. Diffusion of gases occurs through the air filled pore space as well as through the water-filled pores. Diffusion through the air-filled pores is much more rapid but, as roots are thought to be covered by thin water layers, diffusion through water may also limit the oxygen supply required for root respiration. A measure of the oxidation state of a soil is the redox potential: it is a useful characteristic in anaerobic, waterlogged soils. The rate of oxygen diffusion may be measured by the oxygen electrode: measurements made with the oxygen electrode on saturated soils are easy to interpret. In unsaturated soils the interpretation becomes less simple; but the problems of aeration are usually more serious in near-saturated soils.

CHAPTER 3

THE IONIC ENVIRONMENT
OF PLANT ROOTS

In the previous chapter the solutes contained in the water that fills the soil pore space were neglected, except for their effect on the soil moisture potential. Soil water, even in nonsaline soils is, however, not pure water but an electrolyte solution. This solution is dilute: the sum of the concentrations of all the ions is usually in the molar range 10^{-3} to 10^{-2} whereas the concentration of the most abundant ions are commonly of the order of 10^{-4} to 10^{-3} molar. The composition of the solution is very different not only among soils, but also varies with time and depth of sampling within any one profile. The composition of the soil solution of a wide range of soils is shown in table 3.1. Apart from carbon, oxygen and

Table 3.1

Range of ionic compositions of soil solutions

Ion	Range in soils (mmoles/litre)
Ca^{2+}	0.5–38
Mg^{2+}	0.7–100
K^+	0.2–10
$NO_3^- + NH_4^+$	0.16–55
$H_2PO_4^- + HPO_4^-$	0.001–1
SO_4^{2-}	0.1–150
Cl^-	0.2–230
Na^+	0.4–150

(See p.19 of reference 1 for this chapter).

hydrogen, which occur in the plant environment as carbon dioxide and water respectively, thirteen elements are known to be essential for higher plants (nitrogen, phosphorus, sulphur, potassium, calcium, magnesium, iron, manganese, zinc, copper, boron, molybdenum and chlorine). All these elements occur in ionic form in the soil solution. Among those listed in table 3.1, calcium, magnesium and potassium are cations, whereas chloride, sulphate and phosphate are anions; nitrogen occurs in the soil solution either as the ammonium cation or as the nitrate anion. The remaining six elements not listed in the table are usually present and are required by plants only in trace quantities. Although their chemistry in the soil is much less well known than that of the more common elements, they also enter plant roots as ions or as parts of complex ions. It may be mentioned that virtually all major ionic components of common occurrence in soil solution have been shown by solution culture experiments to be essential for higher plants with the possible exception of sodium and silicon; these two elements do occur in plants grown on natural soils but most of them can be grown successfully in culture solutions containing no detectable amounts of either.

Although the soil solution does contain all the essential nutrients ions required by plants, the amounts of these ions present in solution at any one time are small and would soon be depleted by growing plants were it not for the processes whereby the solution is continuously replenished from the soil solid phase. A description of the ionic environment of plants must therefore be concerned with the ionic equilibria involving the nutrient ions in the soil solution and the soil solid phase, the rates of movement of ions in the soil and with methods for characterizing the ability of soils to supply nutrients to plants.

3.1 CATION EQUILIBRIA IN SOILS

Cation exchange

For practical purposes it is convenient to consider the cations of interest for plant nutrition in the soil solid phase to be either *exchangeable* or *nonexchangeable.* From the point of view of the energy of binding of these ions to the soil solids there may not be much justification for such a distinction since in a soil sample in true physicochemical equilibrium the binding energy of all cations of any one type to the soil solid phase is uniform by definition. This does not mean, however, that the rate of movement of any one cation within the soil solid phase or into the soil solution need be the same from all parts of the soil solids, if the equilibrium were disturbed for some reason. The rates do indeed differ to such an extent that it is relatively easy to distinguish both chemically and biologically between those cations that are exchangeable and those which are not. Some aspects of cation exchange have already been discussed in connection with the surface properties of clay minerals. The phenomenon itself was discovered on whole, natural soils more than a hundred years ago, well before it became possible to clarify the origins of the process on the basis of the detailed knowledge of soil materials referred to in chapter 1. Early observations have shown that the quantity of cations removed from a soil sample by leaching with a salt solution exceeds that removed by leaching with pure water. This excess displacement of cations was shown to be accompanied by a retention of approximately equivalent amounts of cations from the displacing salt solution. It has also been shown that although this cation displacement is initially a fast process, its rate is soon reduced to very low levels while large quantities of the types of ions at first rapidly displaced are still present in the soil. This process of cation replacement is *cation exchange* (or, more ambiguously, *base exchange*); the cations involved are known as *exchangeable cations.*

The common types of exchangeable cations found in soils are calcium, magnesium and potassium, in decreasing order of abundance. Hydrogen, aluminium and sodium also occur in exchangeable form; when present in large quantities, these cations raise special problems which will be discussed separately. Values of the total cation exchange capacity (CEC) are usually in the range of 1 to 50 milliequivalents per 100 gram in mineral soils and over 100 milliequivalents per 100 gram soil in organic soils. The exchangeable cations are sometimes divided into hydrogen ions and metallic cations; the percentage of the total CEC neutralized by metallic cations is the *percentage base saturation.*

The basic problem in the estimation of the cation-exchange capacity is that of including all the exchangeable ions in the estimate and excluding all other ions as far as possible. A wide range of methods is now available, from rapid tests yielding approximate results to more sophisticated and usually more laborious methods capable of fairly high precision. The principle of the classical ammonium acetate method has been outlined on page 15. The pH of the saturating ammonium acetate solution is usually adjusted to 7.0; solutions of higher pH, for instance molar sodium acetate at pH 8.2 are used to saturate samples of calcareous soils. The solubility of the calcium carbonate in the soil is minimized in this way.

The isotope-dilution method, as described on page 16, is perhaps the most free from ambiguities and is therefore appropriate if precise data are required. There is usually fairly good agreement between CEC values obtained for samples of the same soil as measured by the ammonium acetate method and by the isotope dilution technique. This confirms that the difference between exchangeable and nonexchangeable cations in any one soil is, at least operationally, fairly distinct. If, however, a range of soil samples of different types is considered, the results are only approximately independent of the method of measurement. This is not unexpected if it is remembered that the difference between exchangeable and nonexchangeable cations of the same type is one of release rates, or kinetics. It would therefore be expected that, over longer periods of time, some of the nonexchangeable cations would also reach the soil solution and replenish the exchange sites depleted of nutrient cations. This has indeed been confirmed particularly for potassium and will be discussed later in this chapter in connection with cation fixation.

Another approximate method for estimating the CEC is based on simple pH measurements. The procedure consists of suspending a soil sample of known weight in a known volume of a fairly concentrated solution of acetic acid of known pH. Some hydrogen ions are then taken out of solution by ion exchange with the metallic cations of the soil, resulting in an increase of pH. This pH rise, after equilibrium has been reached, is a measure of the amount of exchangeable cations in the soil. Titration of the original acetic acid solution with strong alkali is used for direct calibration. An analogous procedure is used for estimating the amount of exchangeable hydrogen ions: the soil sample is suspended in neutral ammonium acetate and the pH drop on equilibration is measured. This method is rapid and suitable for routine use with large numbers of samples; it can therefore be used in advisory work.

The affinity of the charged surfaces of soil solids for cations is indicated approximately by the selectivity coefficient referred to on page 14. The true measure of the free energy of cation exchange, ΔG_e, which is the difference between the free energies of adsorption of a pair of cations, is related to the ion exchange constant K_e by the expression

$$\Delta G_e = -RT \ln K_e$$

The ion-exchange constant is the equilibrium constant of a cation-exchange process, for instance

$$[N^+]_{soln} + [M^+]_{ads} \rightleftharpoons [N^+]_{ads} + [M^+]_{soln}$$

according to the mass-action equation

$$\frac{[N^+]_{ads}\,[M^+]_{soln}}{[M^+]_{ads}\,[N^+]_{soln}} = K_e$$

where the quantities in brackets are the activities of the ions concerned. An equilibrium constant, or an ion-exchange constant as just defined, is a true constant for a given exchanger and a given pair of ions; it is independent of the concentration of the ions in the solution or of the mole ratio of the adsorbed ions, whereas the selectivity coefficient may, and usually does, vary as a function of these variables. The measurement of the ion-exchange constant would obviously be preferable to that of the selectivity coefficient. Not only is the ion-exchange constant directly related to the free energy of ion exchange (which the selectivity coefficient is not), but the constancy of the measured ion-exchange property over a wide range of exchanger compositions also allows the predictive use of such values for practical purposes, for instance in irrigation. Evaluation of the ion-exchange constant calls for the measurement of the activities of ions both in the solution and on the exchanger. The problems associated with measurements of ion activities in solution are relatively minor ones, especially if the ionic composition of the solution is known in detail. The activity of the adsorbed ions is, however, much less easily accessible. The best procedure is to measure the selectivity coefficients for the exchange reaction at various exchanger compositions and at different ionic strengths, followed by extrapolation of the results to infinite dilution to obtain a range of values for the selectivity coefficient. These values are then averaged over all exchanger compositions to give the *thermodynamic ion-exchange constant.*

Any models trying to explain the behaviour of the adsorbed ions would then have to explain the measured changes in selectivity coefficient with exchanger composition. A particularly simple assumption about the state of the adsorbed ions is to regard them as forming a two-dimensional solid solution at the surface of the exchanger. The activities of the adsorbed ions then become proportional to their mole fractions. One of the oldest ion-exchange equations, that of Vanselow, is based on this assumption. More refined models of cation exchange take into account the geometry of the charged sites on the planar clay surfaces. Another equation, that of Gapon, is also used extensively. This can be formulated as

$$\frac{(M^+)_{ads}\ [N^{2+}]^{\frac{1}{2}}_{soln}}{(N^{2+})_{ads}\ [M^+]_{soln}} = K_G$$

where the parentheses represent the equivalent fractions of the adsorbed ions and the brackets are ion concentrations in solution. This equation which is empirical and has little theoretical foundation, is useful because K_G is usually found to be constant for soils over a wide range of exchanger compositions.

Cation fixation
Another process, which involves cations and the soil solid phase, and is related to cation exchange is *cation fixation.* Broadly defined, cation fixation is the reduction of exchangeability or extractability of cations due to interactions with the soil solid phase. Potassium is the cation best known for its tendency to become fixed, but it is not the only one as is shown in figure 3.1. Fixation, for the purpose of this diagram, is defined as the reduction of the extractability of the experimental cation by a fixed quantity of hydrochloric acid, following drying of the soil clay sample at 100°C. This procedure serves to emphasize the differences in the interaction of each type of cation with the soil solids on drying and to diminish the effect of the difference between the extractability of the different cations with hydrochloric acid. The figure shows that whereas potassium is the cation fixed to the largest extent, it is not the only one; the ammonium cation, another important nutrient ion, is fixed to almost the same degree and all the ions tested were subject to at least some fixation.

The nature of cation fixation is of practical interest in plant nutrition. The soil materials most commonly associated with potassium fixation are the mica-type soil clays known as *illites.* In these mica-type minerals the interlayer cations balancing the negative charges on the clay crystals are predominantly potassium ions which are partly embedded into the hexagonal depressions between the oxygen atoms of the unit layer surfaces. The explanation of fixation seems to be the good stereochemical

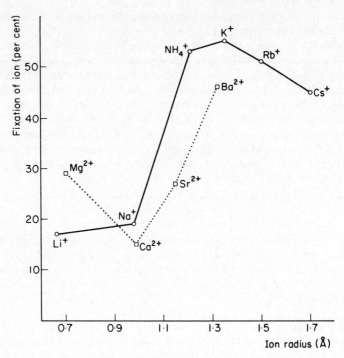

Figure 3.1 Effect of ion size and valency on the fixation of cations by a soil clay (Data of J. B. Page and L. D. Baver, *Proc., Soil Sci. Soc. Am.*, 4 (1939), 150.

fit between these hexagonal depressions and the potassium or ammonium ions, which may lose some of their water of hydration in the course of fixation. It is sometimes possible by suitable techniques to extract the potassium from a mica and to replace it with other cations. This process is accompanied by swelling of the clay as water molecules penetrate between the unit layers. The expanded mineral, containing exchangeable cations instead of potassium, is known as *vermiculite*. It is also possible to convert vermiculites to micas by treatments with solutions containing potassium ions. The mineral then shrinks and the basal spacing collapses, as observed by X-ray diffraction, fixing the potassium ions in the interlayer regions. As has been discussed, potassium and ammonium are not the only cations fixed by soil minerals, nor is cation fixation unique to illitic clays. Involvement of other clays would be expected if the mechanism of fixation involved the charged basal surfaces of micas with depressions in the layer of hexagonally arrayed surface oxygen atoms: such surface pattern is common to all 2:1 type clay minerals. It has indeed been found that montmorillonite does fix some cations, particularly potassium ions, but the extent of fixation is much lower than for vermiculite. There are two reasons for this: (1) the surface charge density of vermiculites is much higher than that of montmorillonites, resulting in more 'links' per unit area between adjacent sheets of vermiculite via shared interlayer potassium ions than between the montmorillonite layers; (2) the isomorphous substitution in montmorillonite is predominantly octahedral, whereas in vermiculite it is primarily tetrahedral, thereby making the electrostatic interactions between the layers and the interlayer cations stronger in vermiculite than in montmorillonite.

An important factor affecting potassium fixation is the degree to which the soil is dried prior to the estimation of fixation. For vermiculite, containing exchangeable cations other than potassium, the basal spacing is about 1.4 nm. On potassium saturation, the basal spacing is reduced to about 1.2 nm; some of the water must therefore have been squeezed out from between the layers. Some but not all of the interlayer potassium becomes nonexchangeable on this treatment. Drying the potassium saturated clay at room temperature or higher reduces the basal spacing to about 1.0 nm; more of the interlayer potassium now becomes fixed. Montmorillonite also fixes some potassium on drying, but the basal spacings usually remain higher than for vermiculite subjected to the same treatment and the fixation process is more easily reversible than for vermiculite.

It is instructive to examine the relationship between potassium fixation and the degrees of potassium saturation of the cation exchange capacity. It has been observed that fixation of added potassium by soils is inversely related to the potassium saturation of the exchange capacity: soils containing higher percentages of exchangeable potassium fix less added potassium than those that are low in exchangeable potassium. Fixation of added potassium seems to become important below a potassium saturation value of about 4 per cent. A relationship of this kind would indeed be expected and indicates that the free energy of potassium adsorption on exchange sites becomes comparable with that of fixed potassium when the potassium saturation drops below about 4 per cent; above this value, the free energy of adsorption to exchange sites is less negative than that of fixation. In a hypothetical, completely potassium-depleted soil, added potassium will be fixed, and about 4 per cent of the exchange sites will become potassium saturated approximately simultaneously. If further potassium is added, it will be retained in exchangeable form.

The availability of fixed potassium to plants has been widely investigated. In short-term experiments of up to a few weeks duration, plants derive potassium mainly from exchangeable sources; in long-term experiments, extending over several growing seasons, plants draw on fixed potassium too, if no fertilizer potassium is added. This is not unexpected in view of what has been said about the mechanisms of potassium exchange and fixation.

Soil acidity

Another phenomenon related to cation equilibria in soils is soil acidity. Acids and bases have been defined by Brønsted and Lowry as proton donors and acceptors respectively; a broader definition, that of Lewis, regards acids as electron acceptors and bases as electron donors. The acid-base properties of soils are due to the presence of acids and bases both of the Brønsted–Lowry type and of the Lewis type. The main examples of the former are the carboxyl and phenolic hydroxyl groups of the humic and fulvic acids. Cation-exchange sites neutralized by exchangeable hydrogen ions can also be regarded as Brønsted acids in a wider sense. The commonest examples of Lewis acids in soils are the aluminium ions exposed at the edges of clay crystallites and also the exchangeable aluminium ions. It has been debated for a long time whether the acidity (low pH) of a neutral salt extract of a soil derives directly from exchangeable hydrogen ions displaced from the soil or whether it is due to the hydrolysis in the salt solution of exchangeable aluminium ions displaced from the soil. It is now known that, while H^+-saturated clays can be prepared by suitable methods, they are more or less unstable and in due course spontaneously convert into Al^{3+} clays. Aluminium is indeed found extensively as an exchangeable cation in acid soils: below pH 5, one third or more of the cation exchange capacity of a mineral soil is usually saturated with aluminium ions.

The information derivable from soil pH measurements is of two kinds. A single pH measurement on a soil suspension gives the concentration (or, strictly, the activity) of the hydrogen ions in a solution in equilibrium with the soil. A measurement of this kind gives an indication of the momentary acidity of the soil. Two or more pH measurements are necessary for determining the titratable soil acidity which is the amount of base required to bring the soil to a predetermined pH value. Titratable acidity, which is related to the lime requirement, can be measured in two ways: either the soil pH is adjusted to the required pH by successive measured additions of base to a soil sample suspended in water, or a solution of a known amount of buffer at the required pH is added to the soil and the drop in pH on equilibrium is measured, as in the procedure for the determination of exchangeable hydrogen, described on page 74.

The measurement of a soil pH by means of the universally available electrode assemblies and pH meters is a simple operation in the laboratory, or even in the field. Accordingly, pH is probably the most frequently measured property of soils. However, it must be remembered that a soil (or, more appropriately, a soil suspension) has no unique pH value; the pH is a function of many variables. Usually the most important factor affecting the measured pH value of a soil is the concentration of the salt solution in which the soil is suspended for pH measurement. The higher this concentration, the lower the recorded pH. This effect is primarily due to the displacement of exchangeable hydrogen and aluminium ions from the soil solids by the cations of the salt solution. Thus, the pH of a soil may be one pH unit lower in molar neutral potassium chloride than in distilled water. Soils always contain some soluble salts and these will likewise produce a variation in the measured soil pH with varying soil/water ratio if the soil sample is suspended in water for the pH measurement. Attempts to avoid dilution and to measure the pH of a soil paste rather than of a soil suspension may yield unreliable results due to an unwanted potential — the so-called *liquid-junction potential* — arising at the junction of the soil paste and the reservoir of the reference electrode (figure 3.2). The liquid junction may also become blocked by soil particles if the reference electrode is pressed into the soil paste and under such

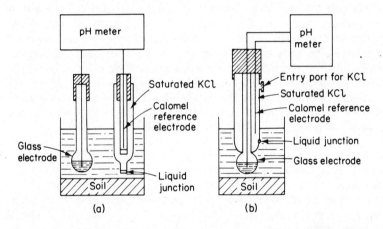

Figure 3.2   Electrode assemblies for pH measurement

(a) Glass electrode/calomel electrode assembly; (b) combined glass and calomel electrodes.

conditions of open circuit meaningful results cannot be obtained. Therefore it is always advisable to make a pH measurement by immersing the electrodes, in particular the reference electrode with the liquid junction, into the supernatant solution rather than into the soil paste. Biologically produced carbonic and nitric acids also affect the pH of a soil. When reporting the results of a soil pH measurement, the conditions such as the soil/solution ratio and the concentration of the suspending soil solution should always be indicated. 10^{-2} molar calcium chloride is often used as the suspending electrolyte, on the grounds that the concentration of the soil solution itself is usually of this order. A convenient and often used soil/solution ratio is 1:2.5 by weight. The soil/solution ratio is more critical when water is used for equilibration rather than a salt solution such as calcium chloride. Care should be taken to obtain representative average soil samples from the area under consideration. Poor sampling technique can account for otherwise unexplainable relatively large pH differences.

Soil pH and plant performance are interrelated but many factors are involved and the relationship between them is neither direct nor simple. Moderate hydrogen ion concentrations themselves usually do not limit plant growth. Many plants can be grown satisfactorily in nutrient solutions of pH 4.5, although higher hydrogen-ion concentrations do inhibit the proper functioning of plant roots, especially at low calcium-ion concentrations. Acid soils, however, do contain ions such as aluminium and manganese, the toxicity of which has been confirmed at low concentrations in nutrient solutions. Manganese toxicity often occurs in acid soils after steam sterilization: steaming significantly increases the soluble and exchangeable manganese content of soils, so the pH of steamed soils needs careful control. The phosphate supply of plants grown on acid soils is usually less adequate than that of plants growing in neutral soils; the same holds for molybdenum. On the other hand the potential supply of iron, manganese, zinc, copper and boron decreases with increasing soil pH. The optimum pH, to which soils are adjusted, if necessary, by liming is in the region of 6.5; this figure is somewhat arbitrary and represents a compromise pH value at which the overall supply of all nutrients is believed to be optimal.

Soil salinity

Salinity is a further characteristic of certain soils which is related to soil/cation interactions. Soils or growth media are described as saline if they contain excess soluble salts, for instance sodium chloride or calcium sulphate and/or sodium as exchangeable cation in excess of a certain maximum value. Excess soluble salts in general, and sodium in particular, are undesirable for several reasons and if present, may limit plant growth. The methods for evaluating the soluble salt content of soils, the behaviour of sodium as an exchangeable cation, and some possible explanations of the adverse effects of salinity on plant growth will now be discussed.

Ions are charged particles able to carry current in an electrolyte solution; the conductivity of such a solution is therefore related to the concentration of ions in the solution. The difference between the conductivities of ions of the same valency are not great (with the exception of hydrogen and hydroxyl ions which are significantly better conductors than other ions) so that as a rough approximation the conductivity of a solution can be used to estimate its electrolyte concentration. The conductivity of a conductor such as an electrolyte solution does of course depend on the dimensions of the conductor. Results of conductivity measurements are therefore corrected for this and are expressed as specific conductance, in units of reciprocal ohm cm^{-1} or mho cm^{-1}. Other, more convenient units are the millimho cm^{-1} or the micromho cm^{-1}. Instruments for measuring conductivities in horticultural practice are sometimes calibrated in units of Cf (1 Cf = 100 micromho cm^{-1}). The empirical relationship between the concentration of an 'average' mixed salt solution and its conductivity is given in figure 3.3. If

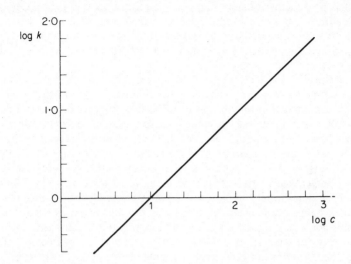

Figure 3.3 Empirical relationship between the concentration c and the specific conductivity k of an 'average' mixed salt solution at 25°C. Concentrations in millequivalents litre^{-1}, conductivities in millimho cm^{-1}.
(See p.364 of general reference 1).

the soil solution is not saturated with respect to a salt present in the soil, the measured concentration or conductivity of the extract will depend on the amount of water added to the soil prior to measurement. The soil/solution ratio must therefore be specified if the conductivity figures are to be compared with previously determined tolerance limits of plants. In one conventional procedure, the soil is adjusted to saturation with water and the conductivity of the saturation extract is measured. As a general guide 4 millimho cm^{-1} in a saturation extract, corresponding to a concentration of about 45 millinormal, may be regarded as the limit distinguishing saline soils from nonsaline ones. This limit is quite arbitrary; the yield of salt-sensitive plants, such as beans and lettuce may be halved by such salinity levels, whereas salt-tolerant crops such as beet or spinach may hardly be affected.

As has already been mentioned, all ions contribute to the conductivity of the soil extract, but not all are equally injurious to plants. Calcium sulphate in particular may accumulate, especially under greenhouse conditions of intensive fertilizer application but ions of this salt are relatively harmless to plants. The concentration of a saturated solution of calcium sulphate is about 30 millimolar at 25°C. To exclude the contribution of this salt from the measured conductivity, the water which is added to the soil before conductivity measurement may be presaturated with calcium sulphate. This precaution has the effect of preventing the dissolution of further calcium sulphate from the soil and of precipitating it if present in the soil solution. Such measurements, if corrected for by subtracting the conductivity of the saturated calcium sulphate solution itself, give the concentration of potentially detrimental salts in the soil extract.

In addition to the concentration of soluble salts, the extent of sodium saturation of the exchange capacity is also of interest. As a tolerable upper limit of sodium saturation, 15 per cent has been suggested. Higher values than this are undesirable, because the soil crumbs become liable to deflocculation with a resulting drastic fall in the hydraulic conductivity of the soil unless the concentration of salt in the soil is kept high. A problem often arising in this connection is that of predicting the exchangeable sodium percentage in a soil that is to be irrigated for a prolonged period with irrigation water of known composition. This is essentially a cation-exchange equilibrium problem and can be solved as such. Small columns are set up in the laboratory and the irrigation water with a known *sodium-adsorption ratio* (SAR) is applied repeatedly. The sodium-adsorption ratio represents the ionic composition of the irrigation water and is defined as

$$\frac{m_{Na^+}}{(m_{Ca^{2+}} + m_{Mg^{2+}})^{1/2}}$$

where the molarities are usually expressed in units of millimoles per litre. The term 'sodium adsorption ratio' for this quantity is misleading since it implies adsorbed ions, whereas ions in solution are involved. After a large number of irrigations, the exchangeable ions are removed from the soil sample and the *exchangeable sodium ratio* (ESR) is determined. The exchangeable sodium ratio is the equivalent fraction of sodium on the soil exchange complex

$$ESR = \frac{ES}{CEC - ES}$$

where ES and CEC are the amounts of exchangeable sodium and the total cation exchange capacity respectively, in units of milliequivalents per 100 gram soil. If ESR is plotted against SAR for each of the experimental soils, a straight line is usually obtained, the slope of which is the exchange constant K_G in Gapon's equation (see page 75). In spite of various complicating factors arising under field conditions, this empirical K_G value (together with the measured SAR of irrigation water) is usually found adequate for predicting the ESR and hence the percentage sodium saturation of soils to be irrigated in the field.

The detrimental effects of soluble salts in the soil solution are usually of two types: a general osmotic effect and a specific toxicity of particular ions. The nonspecific osmotic effect is a direct consequence of the increase of the osmotic pressure or solute suction of the soil solution, reducing the rate of water uptake by plants. If this explanation is correct, the effect on water uptake of solutes added to the soil solution should not depend on the nature of the solutes but only on their concentration. In some cases this has been confirmed experimentally.

Under certain conditions, however, plants grown in saline solutions do recover from wilting and regain their original percentage water content. This indicates that a sufficient quantity of ions has been taken up by the plant from the solution to cancel the effect of the increase in osmotic pressure outside the plant. In spite of such self-adjustment, long-term detrimental effects due to solutes in the soil solution may still persist. It has therefore been proposed that such effects may be due to an increase in the osmotic pressure of water *inside* the plant causing an internal water stress.

Specific detrimental effects of salts have also often been observed, most frequently due to sodium and/or chloride. The cause of such specific damage may be the competitive exclusion of a required ion by the ion in excess, or the direct toxic effect of the accumulated ions.

The sensitivity of different plants to soil salinity differs considerably and so do the criteria by which the salt tolerance of plants is assessed in different parts of the world. The U.S. Salinity Laboratory uses the specific conductivity of saturation soil extracts in millimho cm^{-1} at $25°C$ causing a 50 per cent decrease in yield compared to that on a nonsaline, control soil. Using this criterion, the tolerance of horticultural crops to salinity decreases from 12 to about 4 millimho cm^{-1} in the following order: beets, kale, asparagus, spinach, tomato, cabbage, lettuce, potato, cucumber, radish, celery, beans. In the field the effect of soil salinity depends also on other factors, such as the climate and the distribution of salts in the root zone. Detrimental effects are more pronounced in a warm and dry environment than in a cold and humid one; the possibility of uneven distribution of salts should be remembered when sampling soils for salinity measurements.

3.2 SOIL–ANION INTERACTIONS

The chemistry of anions in soils is, on the whole, more complicated than that of cations. The behaviour of cations (at least that of the mono- and most of the divalent ones) is governed primarily by electrostatic forces associated with the extensive negatively charged surfaces of clay particles. Positively charged sites also occur on soil clays, as has already been discussed, but the number of these sites is usually small compared with the negatively charged sites and depends not only on the pH but also on the electrolyte concentration. Purely electrovalent bonds between anions and soil solids (and therefore true anion exchange) are thus of limited importance in most soils. Certain anions, however, such as sulphate and particularly phosphate, do form bonds which are partly ionic and partly covalent in character with the particles in the soil solid phase. It is the diversity of these types of bonds which makes the study of the interaction of soils with some anions rather difficult.

The electrostatic interaction of the extensive negatively charged surfaces on soil materials with anions should result in a repulsion of anions: the concentration of negatively charged ions near the negatively charged surface should be lower than in the bulk solution, distant from the surface. This effect, which is predicted by the theory of the electrical double layer (see page 18), has in fact been observed particularly for monovalent anions such as chloride, for which the independent but interfering process of positive adsorption at positively charged sites on the clay can be minimized under certain conditions. Although the concentration of anions decreases gradually as the negatively charged surface is approached, the negative adsorption can be described schematically by a layer of solution near the surface of area S and thickness X, from which the anions are totally excluded and by a uniform concentration c_o everywhere outside this volume. It is then possible to estimate the negatively charged surface area of the clay S from the expression

$$S = \frac{V_t \, \Delta c}{c_o} \; \frac{1}{X}$$

where V_t is the total volume of the system, Δc is the measured increase in anion concentration due to the introduction of the solid phase and X is the thickness of the anion-free layer near the surface which can be calculated from the theory of the electrical double layer. This method has sometimes been used to measure the surface area of clays, but, due to the uncertainties attending the calculation of the thickness of the excluded layer, the method is probably more suited to testing the assumptions regarding the properties of the electrical double layer at clay surfaces using clays with well-characterized surface areas than for estimating the unknown surface areas of clay materials.

One of the important monovalent anions for plant nutrition is *nitrate*. Inorganic soil materials interact with nitrate very weakly; this may result from cancellation of the effects of negative adsorption at the basal surfaces of clays and the slight positive adsorption at positively charged sites. The main soil reservoir of nitrogen for plants is the organic material of soils and atmospheric nitrogen. The rate of nitrate production from either of these sources is controlled by microbiological rather than physicochemical processes. At one time it was thought that nitrate was the only form of nitrogen which plants could utilize. It is now known that ammonium can also be taken up and may indeed serve as the only nitrogen source in water culture.

As has been seen, the ammonium cation is retained by soils while the nitrate anion is not. Application of ammonium as a fertilizer does therefore have certain advantages in practice over nitrate which is readily leached from the soil without a growing plant cover. Any ammonium applied to the soil is, however, soon oxidized under aerobic soil conditions to nitrite and then to nitrate; these microbiological processes are known as *nitrification*. Some success has been obtained by the use of selective inhibitors of the nitrification processes: one example of such an inhibitor is 2-chloro-6-trichloromethyl pyridine,

$$Cl_3C\text{—}\underset{N}{\bigcirc}\text{—}Cl$$

but other compounds are also under consideration.

The most common divalent nutrient anion is sulphate. In the absence of specific effects, the affinity of surfaces with positively charges sites should be higher for divalent than for monovalent anions. The adsorption of sulphate on soils has indeed often been observed particularly in soils of low pH where the number of positive sites on soil materials is expected to be highest. The process, however, is almost certainly not restricted to anion exchange; other mechanisms, such as the replacement of surface hydroxyl ions in iron and aluminium oxides and the adsorption of sulphate through exchangeable calcium ions have also been suggested. Apart from the surfaces of the inorganic soil solids, soil organic matter is also a reservoir of sulphate. Microbial decomposition or mineralization of soil organic matter therefore contributes to the sulphate supply of plants, and so does the sulphate contained in rainwater. The problems of sulphate supply have so far not been studied as extensively as for instance those of phosphate, because, although the amount of sulphur removed by an average annual crop from the soil is often of the same order as that of phosphorus, the rate of sulphate supply by soils to plants is high enough to be seldom limiting.

Phosphorus is present in the soil solution as the orthophosphate anion which is derived from orthophosphoric acid H_3PO_4, in which the phosphorus atom is surrounded by four oxygen atoms. The distribution of orthophosphate ions of various types in solution is a function of pH and the dissociation constants of phosphoric acid: the relative abundance of $H_2PO_4^-$ and HPO_4^{2-} are shown in figure 3.4. In the physiological pH range dihydrogen phosphate and monohydrogen phosphate are the dominant orthophosphate anions. It might therefore be expected that the behaviour of orthophosphate in soils would be similar to, or intermediate between, that of monovalent and divalent anions such as chloride and sulphate. This, however, is not the case: the concentration of phosphate in the soil solution is usually less by one or two orders of magnitude than that of the

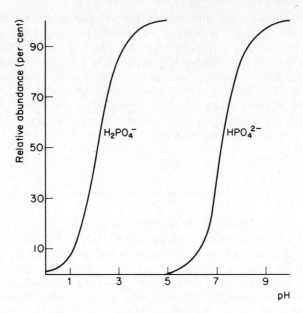

Figure 3.4   Relative abundance of $H_2PO_4^-$ and HPO_4^{2-} ions at various pH values

other anions, and the fraction of fertilizer phosphate utilized in the short term is also much lower than, for example, that of fertilizer nitrogen. The reason for this difference is the high affinity of the orthophosphate anions for the cations on the surfaces of soil solids, resulting in what is known by the somewhat vague term phosphate 'fixation'. Due to the low concentration of phosphate in the soil solution, this solution must be replenished frequently from the soil solids to supply the phosphate needs of plants: the nature of the phosphate in the soil solid phase has therefore been much investigated.

A large proportion (on average, about half) of the total phosphorus in soils is present as orthophosphate esterified to organic compounds. Hydrolysis to inorganic phosphate is, however, rather slow at least in temperate climates. This fact together with the low mobility of the inorganic orthophosphate produced on hydrolysis limits the immediate utility of the organic phosphate compounds for plants, but the phosphorus in organic combination is not permanently lost as a plant nutrient.

Investigations of the nature of the phosphatic materials in the inorganic fraction of the soil are beset with difficulties. The content of total phosphorus in soils is usually rather low; about 0.06 per cent can be regarded as an average value. It is thus only exceptionally possible to detect any known phosphatic minerals such as hydroxyapatite $Ca_5(PO_4)_3OH$ in soils by optical examination or by X-ray diffraction.

Characterization of the inorganic phosphate compounds in soils has therefore mostly been attempted by indirect methods, involving in particular the solubility behaviour of known phosphate compounds and of soil phosphate. Calcium phosphate compounds are known to be highly soluble at low pH but insoluble at high pH values. Iron phosphates exhibit minimum solubility in the neutral pH range, but are soluble in both strong acids and alkalis. Aluminium phosphates are soluble in solutions containing fluoride ions: aluminium forms soluble complex ions with fluoride. Iron oxides, which may entrap phosphate compounds can be dissolved, and the entrapped phosphate released, by solutions of reducing agents such as sodium dithionite. These considerations form the basis of a scheme of consecutive extractions with appropriate solvents, which is assumed to extract phosphate from different types of compounds present in the soil. The first extractant is molar ammonium chloride which normally extracts a small quantity of phosphate regarded as water soluble. The next extraction is with 0.5 molar ammonium fluoride extracting the phosphorus from aluminium phosphates. This is followed by 0.1 molar sodium hydroxide extraction for the iron phosphates; 0.25 molar sulphuric acid is then used to extract calcium phosphates. The last extractant is sodium dithionite in 0.3 molar sodium citrate to extract *occluded phosphates*. The difference between the sum of the phosphate in all the extracts and the total phosphorus in the soil is mostly organic phosphate. The fractionation obtained by this method is rather crude, as phosphate dissolved by any one extractant may reprecipitate in the soil during extraction in other chemical forms. The fractionation is suitable, however, for comparative purposes.

A more ambitious way of using solubility criteria to characterize the inorganic phosphate in the soil solid phase is by the employment of the *solubility product constants* of known phosphate compounds. The solubility product constant is the measured product of the concentrations of ions in the saturated solution of a salt in equilibrium with the solid: the exponent of each ion concentration in the product is the number of the particular ions present in one 'molecule' of salt. For instance, the solubility product of variscite, an aluminium phosphate $AlH_2PO_4(OH)_2$ can be written

$$Sp_v = [Al]\ [H_2PO_4]\ [OH]^2$$

where the quantities in brackets are the activities of the ions in a solution saturated with variscite. The solubility product Sp is independent of the presence of other ions in the solution and for crystals which are not too small, depends only on the temperature. Its value for variscite at room temperature is $10^{-30.5}$. In principle, therefore, the presence or absence of crystalline variscite could be inferred from measurements of the concentrations of aluminium, dihydrogen phosphate and hydroxyl ions in a solution in equilibrium with the soil. In soils containing variscite in the solid phase, the measured ion product should approximate $10^{-30.5}$; in soils not containing variscite, the ion product would be less than this.

To test these ideas the solubility product is usually rearranged; for instance, the solubility product for variscite can be written

$$\tfrac{1}{3}pAl + pH_2PO_4 = 2.5 + 2(pH - \tfrac{1}{3}pAl)$$

where pAl, pH_2PO_4 and pH are the negative logarithms of the concentrations or strictly, activities of the respective ions. In rearranging the solubility product, the ion product of water, $pH + pOH = 14$, has been applied. Experimental data can now be expressed by plotting $\tfrac{1}{3}pAl + pH_2PO_4$ against $pH - \tfrac{1}{3}pAl$. For soils in which variscite is present in the solid phase, the points should fall on a straight line with a slope of 2 and an intercept of 2.5. Results obtained in this way on a group of acid soils are shown in figure 3.5. Although many experimental points do fall near the straight line corresponding to variscite, most are either above the line (signifying undersaturation of the solution with respect to variscite) or below (indicating supersaturation). The diagram in figure 3.5 is drawn on a

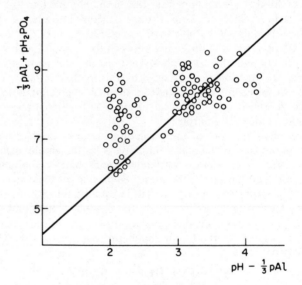

Figure 3.5   Test for the occurrence of variscite $AlH_2PO_4(OH)_2$ in some acid soils
The solid line represents the solubility product of variscite.
(Data of B. C. Wright and M. Peech, *Soil Sci.*, 90, (1960), 32.

logarithmic scale; the deviations from the line are therefore substantial, each scale division representing a tenfold or a hundredfold variation in the quantities plotted on the horizontal and vertical axes respectively. The results indicate that crystalline variscite with solubility product $10^{-30.5}$

does not occur in most of the soils tested. Undersaturation could simply be interpreted as an indication of the absence of variscite from the soil solids. Apparent supersaturation may be explained, for instance, by possible overestimates of the measured ion products due to the presence of soluble *complex ions* of aluminium and/or phosphate in solution or by the presence of variscite-like microcrystals in the soil, the solubility product of which would exceed $10^{-30.5}$, the value for macrocrystalline variscite.

Similar measurements can be made on soils in the neutral and slightly alkaline range to test for the presence of known calcium phosphate compounds, particularly dicalcium phosphate $CaHPO_4$, octacalcium phosphate $Ca_4H(PO_4)_3$ and hydroxyapatite $Ca_5(PO_4)_3OH$. The difficulties here are even greater than with variscite: the true solubility products of the more basic compounds octacalcium phosphate and hydroxyapatite are difficult to determine unambiguously even in soil-free systems, as the dissolution of the crystals is accompanied by surface reactions. Different solubility products are obtained depending on whether equilibrium is approached from supersaturated or undersaturated conditions. In soil solutions the measured ion products often depend on the soil/solution ratio. Because of these difficulties the results are inconclusive but tend to indicate that, like crystalline aluminium phosphates, calcium phosphates exhibiting the solubility products of macrocrystalline calcium phosphates do not occur in soils. Such compounds could still exist, however, as surface phases in the form of microcrystals or as coatings on soil materials such as clays or aluminium and iron oxides.

The amount of surface phosphate in soils can be estimated by radioisotope dilution methods. If isotopically labelled phosphate (^{32}P or P* for brevity, is a convenient isotope) is mixed with a suspension of crystalline phosphates, the added phosphate comes rapidly into equilibrium with the phosphate in the surface of the solids. The specific activity P*/P is then the same in all phases, that is

$$\frac{(P^*)_{surface}}{(P)_{surface}} = \frac{(P^*)_{solution}}{(P)_{solution}}$$

The amount of nonradioactive surface phosphate, $(P)_{surface}$, can then be estimated from measurements of the remaining three quantities. The principle of this procedure, which is identical to that described on page 16 for the measurement of exchangeable cations, can also be applied to soils but as these are more complex systems than crystalline phosphates, the interpretation of the measurements is often less straightforward.

In soil systems the amount of surface phosphate measured is often not independent of the length of time of contact between the tracer and the soil solids. Isotopic dilution is at first rapid but then continues at a slower rate. This reflects the absence of a sharp distinction between surface and subsurface phosphate in soils, or the inhomogeneous nature of the surfaces containing phosphate. Another difficulty is the low level of nonradioactive phosphate in the solution in equilibrium with the soil to which carrier-free tracer phosphate has been added. This can be overcome, if necessary, by adding nonlabelled carrier phosphate to the soil before equilibration. It has been claimed that this does not alter the amount of measured surface phosphate provided that a long enough equilibration time is allowed. Such independence of the measured amount of surface phosphate from added carrier seems unlikely, however, unless sufficient carrier phosphate is added to saturate all potential phosphate adsorbing surfaces and, in this case, the property measured is not the amount of pre-existing surface soil phosphate.

The amount of soil phosphate measured by the isotope dilution method is known as the E value. Provided that the conditions affecting the result, such as equilibration time, soil/solution ratio and temperature are standardized, the E value gives reproducible results which can be related to the phosphate fertilizer response of plants. Plants can be used directly for sampling the isotopically diluted pool of labile soil phosphate. This will be discussed in section 3.4.

3.3   MOVEMENT OF IONS IN SOILS

Although both the amount of nutrients in the soil solid phase and their energies of binding do affect the ability of soils to supply plants with the required ions, ultimately it is the rates of arrival of these ions at the root surface that determine the adequacy of the nutrient supply. These rates of arrival, or *fluxes*, are not independent of the amounts and binding energies but they depend on many other circumstances in rather intricate ways.

Ions may move in the soil either by diffusion in response to concentration gradients generated by roots, fertilizer application, or mass flow of the water in which the nutrients are dissolved. To maintain electrical neutrality, diffusion of ions must either be accompanied by diffusion of other ions of the same sign in the opposite direction (known as *interdiffusion*) or by movement of ions of opposite sign in the same direction (*salt diffusion*). The diffusion rate is a product of a driving force term, the *concentration gradient*, and a conductivity term, the *diffusion coefficient*. The estimation of these quantities in solutions is relatively easy but in soils it is attended by many difficulties. Estimation of the concentration gradient requires knowledge of the concentration of the bulk soil solution and the concentration at the root surface. While it is usually possible to determine the lower concentration limit to which plants can deplete the solution of a particular ion in solution culture, it does not follow that the concentration in soils will be reduced by plant roots to the same extent. At any rate, the maximum value of the potential gradient can be estimated by assuming that the plant depletes the concentration of a nutrient ion at the root surface to zero. The diffusion coefficient of ions in water can be accurately measured; it is about 10^{-9} m^2 s^{-1} for nutrient ions. In porous media like soils additional variable geometrical and physicochemical factors are superimposed. Because of the presence of the solid phase and of air in part of the pore space, only a fraction of the cross-section is available for the transmission of ions. The tortuosity of the conducting channels also reduces the measured diffusion coefficient and so does the increased viscosity of water near solid surfaces. Interaction of the ions with the surface (negative or positive adsorption) also affects the diffusion coefficient.

In relatively simple systems of montmorillonite gels saturated with a single exchangeable cation such as Li^+ or Cs^+, the measured electrical conductivity of the gel can be accounted for in terms of the tortuosity effect and of the diffusion coefficient of the adsorbed exchangeable ions. The diffusion coefficient of ions in the bulk solution increases from lithium to caesium, while the surface diffusion coefficient decreases in the same order, with the decrease in the radius of the hydrated ions. The values of diffusion coefficients in soils for nutrient ions reported by different workers are generally in the range of 10^{-11} to 10^{-13} $m^2 s^{-1}$ and depend not only on the mobility of the adsorbed ions but also markedly on the soil-moisture tension and on soil compaction.

Ions also move in soils as a result of the mass flow of soil water. In the growing season the direction and extent of the net movement of those ions not adsorbed by the soil due to mass flow depend on the relative magnitudes of *precipitation* and *evapotranspiration*. Net downward movement occurs only when precipitation exceeds evapotranspiration. In humid regions, monthly rainfall is about 100 mm; transpiration of a good average crop will be of the same order of magnitude. Nutrients are therefore unlikely to be lost from the root zone by leaching during the growing season in humid areas. Under drier conditions, salt may even accumulate. Loss of nutrients due to leaching however, may occur in the tropics where rainfall is heavy and in humid regions during periods when the soil is not supporting a growing crop.

The question of the relative importance of the movement of nutrients to plant roots by mass flow and by diffusion has received much attention but, because of the uncertainties attending the estimation of some of the quantities involved (such as concentration gradients and diffusion coefficients), only very approximate general conclusions can be drawn. The amount of nutrients reaching plant roots in the water transpired can be calculated quite simply. Considering that the evapotranspiration of an average crop amounts to about 300–350 mm and taking into account the range of concentrations of nutrients in the soil solution (table 3.1) it can be shown that the quantity of soil solution transpired usually does contain the calcium and magnesium requirements of an average crop, and often of potassium. The phosphorus supply is, however, usually inadequate. Such calculation does not imply that transpiration and ion uptake by roots are directly linked processes but only that the estimated quantity of ions do reach the surfaces of roots. It seems that the supply of ions which are either not strongly adsorbed by soils or are present in relatively large quantities (such as nitrate, chloride, calcium and magnesium) is determined by the mass flow of the soil solution. However in the supply of those ions that are strongly adsorbed or present in relatively small amounts (such as phosphate and molybdenum) diffusion is important. The position of potassium is intermediate, with either mass flow or diffusion controlling supply depending on circumstances.

3.4   CHARACTERIZATION OF PLANT NUTRIENT SUPPLY

Methods for the characterization of soils with respect to their ability to supply plants with nutrients are necessary for the improvement of our understanding of the processes involving plant nutrients in the soil, and also for predicting the probable plant response to applied fertilizers in the field or greenhouse. Such methods always involve, at some stage, work in the laboratory, the greenhouse and in the field. Laboratory methods establish a certain property of a nutrient ion in a soil reproducibly and relatively quickly. Measurements on plants grown in the greenhouse serve to indicate the fraction of the nutrient which has been available to the particular plant grown under experimental conditions. Similar plant response can be measured in the field, where many further variables are introduced — among them the volume of soil available to each plant. Modern laboratory experiments for the improvement of the understanding of soil processes are usually designed explicitly to investigate (1) the quantity of a particular nutrient in the available pool, (2) the energy with which the nutrient is bound to the soil solids, or (3) the rate at which the nutrient is supplied to the plants. Methods for practical prediction, on the other hand, seek to establish good statistical correlations between a rapidly and simply measured soil property and the plant response in as wide a range of soils as possible, without particular reference to whether the measured soil property reflects a quantity, an energy or a rate parameter. The loss of information involved in neglecting these details are not too serious within a group of closely related soils because the quantity of an 'available' nutrient, its energy of binding and rate of release are roughly related to each other. The use of these practical methods is, however, restricted to a more or less narrow range of soils. Each type of method does therefore have its advantages and limitations and serves under appropriate conditions. Examples of each type of measurement will now be examined to illustrate the principles involved.

One of the parameters determining the supply of nutrients to plants is the size of the labile pool of the particular ion or the amount of nutrient in the soil in a 'labile' form. This quantity is most distinct for monovalent or divalent cations which are adsorbed to the surfaces of soil particles primarily by electrostatic forces. The amount of nutrient in exchangeable form can then be taken to be a measure of the labile pool. Even in this simplest case, however, the distinction between labile and nonlabile is somewhat arbitrary and reflects differences in the rates of equilibration of the nutrient bound to the soil with that in an external solution. If a long enough time scale is considered, nonexchangeable nutrients will also be taken up by plants and thus become available by definition. The size of the labile pool of a nutrient is therefore not a soil property which can be defined without reference to the way in which it has been measured.

The situation is similar for anions such as phosphate. The mechanism of binding of phosphate to the soil solids is poorly understood; it is still possible, however, to obtain an estimate of the labile pool of soil phosphorus by a modification of the isotope-dilution technique, discussed on page 89. If a fertilizer containing labelled phosphorus is mixed with a soil, the radioactive phosphorus will become diluted by that amount of soil phosphorus with which the fertilizer phosphate has come to equilibrium. If plants are now grown on the soil, the specific activity $^{32}P/^{31}P$ or $P*/P$ in the plants will be equal to the specific activity of the phosphorus in the labile pool in the soil from which the plant derives its phosphorus,

$$\frac{P*_{fertilizer}}{P_{fertilizer}+P_{labile}} = \frac{P*_{plant}}{P_{plant}}$$

The amount of labile nonradioactive phosphorus in the soil, known as the L value, can be evaluated from the other four measured variables. A requirement for an L value measurement is that the fertilizer be thoroughly mixed with the soil prior to planting so that equilibrium between the fertilizer phosphorus and the labile soil phosphorus can take place. The amount of carrier phosphorus in the added fertilizer is usually kept low to facilitate isotopic exchange with the soil phosphorus. A suitable test plant such as a grass, grown in pots, allows continuous harvesting so that changes in the measured L value with time can be evaluated. The results available show that in some soils, the size of the labile pool apparently increases with time for months; in others, the change with time is less pronounced.

The principles of the estimation of E and L values are analogous; the results obtained are, however, not expected to be identical. The E value has the advantages of speed and convenience of a laboratory method. The L value introduces the plant as a variable into the system, and is the only way in which differences in the size of the labile pool for different plant species can be examined using the isotope-dilution technique.

The success of free-energy properties in characterizing the availability of soil water to plants has encouraged attempts to extend the principle to ionic nutrients as well. The free energy of binding of a single cation such as a potassium ion at an exchange site is not readily measurable, but the free energy of an ion exchange process such as the potassium–calcium exchange is related to the ion-exchange constant (see page 74). This ion-exchange constant $K_{Ca^{2+}}^{K+}$ can be written

$$K_{Ca^{2+}}^{K+} = \frac{[K^+]_{soln} \, [Ca^{2+}]_{ads}^{1/2}}{[K^+]_{ads} \, [Ca^{2+}]_{soln}^{1/2}}$$

where quantities in brackets are the activities of the ions concerned in a suspension of the soil at equilibrium. The ratio of the ion activities in solution (known as the *reduced ion ratio*) is readily measured. The estimation of the activities of the adsorbed ions is more controversial. The necessity for the measurements involving the adsorbed ions can, however, be avoided if a restriction of the general validity of the measurement is accepted and only one particular ratio of adsorbed cations is considered. Under these conditions the ion exchange equation becomes

$$\frac{[K^+]_{soln}}{[Ca^{2+}]_{soln}^{1/2}} = K_{Ca^{2+}}^{K+} \frac{[K^+]_{ads}}{[Ca^{2+}]_{ads}^{1/2}}$$

The reduced ion ratio is therefore related to the true ion exchange constant at a particular ratio of the ions adsorbed. For practical purposes the most relevant adsorbed ion ratio is the one prevailing in the soil at the time of measurement. The reduced ion ratio

$$\frac{[K^+]_{soln}}{[Ca^{2+}]_{soln}^{1/2}}$$

measured in a suspension in equilibrium with the soil under conditions such that the soil neither adsorbs nor releases potassium from the exchange sites is known as the *potassium potential*. It is a measure of the relative energies of binding of potassium and calcium to the soil solids. The potassium potential is often written

$$\frac{[K^+]_{soln}}{[Ca^{2+} + Mg^{2+}]_{soln}^{1/2}}$$

taking into account the presence of magnesium ions as well as calcium in the soil. On acid soils the denominator would include hydrogen and aluminium ions. In analogy with the behaviour of soil water the existence of an exhaustion ion ratio and a critical ion ratio may be expected. The former would represent the lowest value to which plants can reduce a particular ion ratio and below which plant growth would cease. The latter would represent the ratio below which a plant response to added nutrient would be expected. Numerical values for some limiting ion ratios have already been published, but further work is required before they become firmly enough established for general use.

The question of the energy of binding of anions such as phosphate has also received much attention. This energy is related to the concentration of phosphate in a solution in equilibrium with the soil solids. This concentration does, however, vary for any one soil depending on the experimental conditions, such as the concentration of other ions in the equilibrium solution. In an attempt to select a soil property that is related to the energy of phosphate binding but does not depend on the conditions of measurement it has been suggested that the product of the concentrations of calcium and of dihydrogen phosphate in the equilibrium solution, expressed as $\frac{1}{2}pCa + pH_2PO_4$, the so-called *phosphate potential*, be adopted for this purpose. pCa and pH_2PO_4 are the negative logarithms of the activities of the respective ions in the equilibrium solution.

The question then arises, under what conditions would the phosphate potential be expected to be a soil constant, independent of the experimental conditions and depending only on the energy of binding of phosphate in the soil? It can be seen by inspection that the phosphate potential is the negative logarithm of the square root of the ion product of dicalcium phosphate $Ca(H_2PO_4)_2$. If the solubility of phosphate were controlled by dicalcium phosphate in the solid phase, this ion product would equal the square root of the solubility product of dicalcium phosphate and would indeed be independent of the conditions of measurement. Dicalcium phosphate does not, however, occur in the soil solid phase except in fertilizer granules recently added to the soil. If the solubility of soil phosphate is governed by other, more basic calcium phosphates, then the measured phosphate potential would be independent of the individual concentrations of calcium and phosphate only if the ratio of dihydrogen phosphate and calcium ions were the same in the mineral actually in equilibrium with the soil as it is in dicalcium phosphate (that is, 2:1). This cannot be the case, since in all other phosphate minerals the H_2PO_4/Ca ratio is less than 2:1. In view of these considerations the significance of results showing the independence of the measured phosphate potential from the concentrations of calcium or phosphate in solution are uncertain. In evaluating the phosphate potential concept it may be asked whether it represents, as measured, the free energy of all phosphate in the soil solid phase. The answer seems to be negative: the phosphate potential is a measure of the free energy of the compound dicalcium phosphate and, as such, does not represent the free energy of soil phosphate generally. Thus, the phosphate potential would be expected to be related to plant uptake of phosphate only if calcium and dihydrogen phosphate ions could be substituted for each other for uptake by plants. This clearly is not possible. In accord with this conclusion it has been found that phosphate uptake by plants is not related to the phosphate potential, but rather to the concentration of phosphate ions in solution. Expressing results of phosphate concentration measurements in soil solutions in terms of phosphate potentials therefore seems unwarranted.

Another general approach to the estimation of the energy of adsorption which can often be applied to soil phosphate is the use of an *adsorption isotherm* such as that of Langmuir. An adsorption isotherm is the relationship between the amount of adsorbate adsorbed by unit weight of adsorbent and the equilibrium concentration of the adsorbate in the solution. On the basis of certain assumptions concerning the nature of the adsorption process, the Langmuir adsorption isotherm predicts the general shape of the adsorption isotherm leaving two constants which can be evaluated experimentally from the results: the amount of adsorbate adsorbed by unit weight of adsorbent at saturation and the energy of adsorption. The assumptions underlying the Langmuir adsorption isotherm include the independence of the adsorption sites from each other and the constancy of the energy of adsorption at each adsorption site which is invariant with the degree of surface coverage. Thus only a single energy of adsorption is obtained for any one soil irrespectively of the extent of saturation with phosphate, which is clearly a very crude approximation. The procedure is useful, however, to classify soils to which it is applicable in order of phosphate-fixing tendency.

The rates of replenishment of the soil solution, or the kinetics of the reactions involving nutrient ions and soil solids may also limit the supply of nutrients to plants. As has already been pointed out, the importance of cation exchange for plants is due to the rapid rates of exchange; half-times of attainment of cation exchange equilibria vary depending on the type of soil materials and exchangeable cations considered (see page 19). The rate constants k_1 and k_{-1} of the process of binding and release of a nutrient by the soil solid phase

$$N_{soln} \underset{k_{-1}}{\overset{k_1}{\rightleftharpoons}} N_{ads}$$

can be determined from measurements of the rate of binding of a labelled isotope of the nutrient by the soil. The results are interpreted in terms of a reversible first-order reaction and it is assumed that the diffusion of the nutrient from the solid surface into the solution is rapid and thus not rate limiting. This is not necessarily a good approximation. The technique has been applied to the binding of phosphate by soils; the results indicate that phosphate binding consists of several processes occurring more or less simultaneously. It is therefore not realistic to compare rate constants obtained in this way with rates of uptake of phosphate by plants in the field.

In view of the theoretical and practical difficulties just outlined attending the measurement of the quantity, the energy of binding and rate of release of nutrients, practical methods for predicting plant response to applied fertilizers do not attempt to isolate and separately assess the different aspects of the ability of soils to supply plants with nutrients.

Instead, the procedures are more empirical. Soil extracts are prepared in a standardized manner from samples representing a range of soils, with one of a range of extracting solutions. Originally, dilute solutions of acids (such as citric acid) were used to simulate the action of root exudates, but other extractants (such as water, dilute solutions of salts or alkalis) have more recently also been used. The amounts of the nutrients concerned, usually phosphate and potassium, are estimated in the extracts by suitable chemical methods. Plants are then grown in the experimental soils in pots and the uptake of the nutrients by the plants over a suitable period is estimated. The results of plant uptake measurements are compared with the amounts of nutrients released by the different extracting solutions. The extractant that releases quantities of nutrients in best statistical correlation with plant uptake over the widest range of soils is then adopted for use. The technique is then calibrated under field conditions to establish the fertilizer requirements for different crops. Such methods have been used successfully for phosphate and for potassium for many years. No generally applicable method for rapid chemical characterisation of the nitrogen-supplying ability of soils is available. Nitrogen release and fixation are primarily biological processes which it has not yet been possible to simulate successfully by chemical means.

SUMMARY

All essential nutrients, with the exception of carbon, hydrogen and oxygen, occur and are taken up from the plant root environment in ionic form. Potassium, ammonium, calcium and magnesium occur in the soil solution as cations; nitrate, sulphate, phosphate, chloride, molybdate and borate are anions; whereas the transitional elements iron, manganese, zinc and copper occur in the soil solution either as cations or as components of complex ions.

The best-known process involving ions and the surfaces of soil solids is ion exchange. The amount of exchangeable cations per unit weight of soil is the cation-exchange capacity; for a given soil it varies with the pH and with other experimental conditions. The relative affinity of an ion exchanger to a pair of ions can be expressed in terms of the ion-exchange selectivity coefficient. The ion-exchange constant, which is related to the selectivity coefficient, is a measure of the free energy of exchange between a pair of cations.

Cation fixation is a reduction in the exchangeability or extractability of cations following drying or heating of soil materials. Potassium and ammonium are the nutrient cations most prone to fixation, but other cations may also become fixed to a lesser extent. Fixation is a result of partial dehydration of the exchangeable cations and a collapse of the basal spacing of the clay holding the adsorbed cations in the interlayer spaces. Exchangeable potassium is the immediate reserve of potassium for plants.

Fixed potassium may also be released but only over much longer periods. Soil acidity is related to the presence in the soil of acids of both the Brønsted—Lowry type and of the Lewis type. A single pH measurement gives an indication of the momentary acidity of the soil, whereas two or more pH measurements are required for estimating the titratable acidity of soils. pH is not a unique soil property; it varies for any one soil with the conditions of measurement. The detrimental effects of extreme pH values on plant growth are indirect; the optimum pH for plants generally is in the region of 6.5.

The presence of excess soluble salts in the soil or of sodium in the exchange complex is known as soil salinity. The amount of soluble salts in the soil can be estimated by conductivity measurements made on the soil extracts. The degree of sodium saturation expected after prolonged irrigation with water of known ionic composition can be predicted using appropriate cation exchange equations. The harmful effects of solutes on plants derive from a general osmotic effect and from specific toxicity effects. Sodium and chloride ions are the most frequently accumulating harmful ions; calcium and sulphate are relatively harmless.

The chemistry of anions in the soil is, on the whole, more complicated than that of cations. Nitrate and chloride are not appreciably adsorbed by soil particle surfaces and are liable to leaching at moderate rainfall except in soils supporting an actively growing crop. Sulphate is adsorbed more strongly especially in acid soils. Phosphate is very strongly adsorbed by the inorganic fraction of soils. The amount of labile phosphate can be estimated by isotope-dilution techniques; the nature of the inorganic phosphate present in the soil solid phase is not known with certainty.

Ion movements in the soil solution occur due to mass flow of the whole soil solution or to diffusion of ions within it. The relative importance of the two processes is often not clear; mass flow seems to be more important for ions that are not strongly adsorbed or are present in higher concentrations, whereas diffusion may be more important for the strongly adsorbed ions or those present at low concentrations.

Procedures for characterizing soils with respect to their ability to supply plants with nutrients are aimed either at improving our understanding of soil processes involved in plant nutrition or at predicting the probable fertilizer response of plants in a particular situation. The former type of experiment is usually set up to investigate only one aspect of the supply of nutrients to plants, such as the amount of labile nutrient present, the energy with which it is bound to the soil solids, the rate of release from the soil solids to the solution or the rate of movement of ions in the soil by mass flow or by diffusion. The development of methods for the prediction of fertilizer response involves the establishment of a good statistical correlation between a chemical property of the nutrient in the soil which can easily and quickly be measured in the laboratory and a parameter related to plant uptake of the nutrient. Both types of methods have their advantages and are applicable under appropriate conditions.

PART II

HORTICULTURAL PRINCIPLES

CHAPTER 4

MACROSCOPIC STRUCTURE AND PROPERTIES OF GROWTH MEDIA

4.1 FIELD SOILS

A knowledge of the macroscopic properties of soils is essential to the scientist working in the field and to the commercial grower. When an assessment is made in the field, an impression of the soil's origin, texture and structure is obtained; this information will subsequently provide a useful guide as to the 'workability' of a particular field soil and its suitability for particular crops. Similarly, if the land is to be used for amenity, the assessment must indicate its usefulness for particular purposes, such as sports turf.

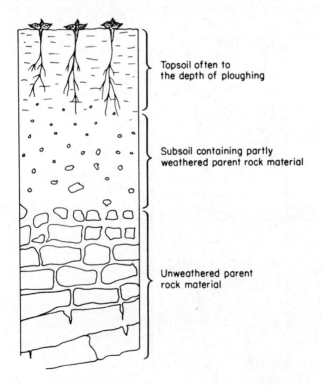

Topsoil often to the depth of ploughing

Subsoil containing partly weathered parent rock material

Unweathered parent rock material

Figure 4.1   Diagramatic representation of a sedentary soil profile

Profiles

When cuttings for road or railway systems or other engineering projects are made, the successive layers of materials forming the soil are exposed. The exposure of these layers *in situ* is called a *profile*. To investigate a soil for horticultural purposes a hole dug with a spade to the depth of about a metre will usually expose an adequate profile; a hole even shallower than this will provide a useful view of the top-soil profile. Boring with a soil auger will often give a good enough idea for a grower of the changes in material down the profile of the upper layers.

The *topsoil*, which is the zone of most interest to horticulturists, has usually been formed over a period of thousands of years and is derived from weathered rock and organic matter accumulated from the remains of plants and animals. It also contains a larger population of living organisms, ranging in size from bacteria to insects and worms, than other soil layers. The percentage organic matter content of soils is usually highest at, or near, the soil surface and decreases with depth. This accounts for the subsoil becoming progressively lighter in colour with increasing depth, until it assumes the visual characteristics of the underlying geological

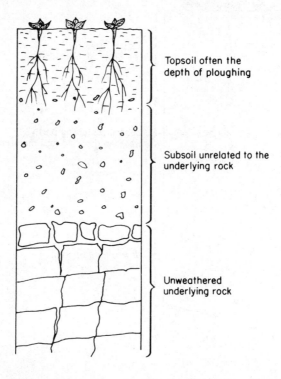

Topsoil often the
depth of ploughing

Subsoil unrelated to the
underlying rock

Unweathered
underlying rock

Figure 4.2   Diagrammatic representation of a transported soil profile

material or parent rock. This visual gradation is particularly obvious when a soil has been formed *in situ* by the gradual weathering of parent rock, such soils being referred to as *sedentary*.

However, many soils of horticultural importance are more complicated in origin because some of the underlying materials have been transported by agents such as glaciers, water or wind and therefore bear no relation to the underlying rock. These are referred to as *transported soils*; examples are clays deposited by glaciers and alluvial soils derived from former river beds.

Horizons

The successive layers in a soil profile are called horizons. Each horizon is designated by a letter, and they are defined as follows (figure 4.3).

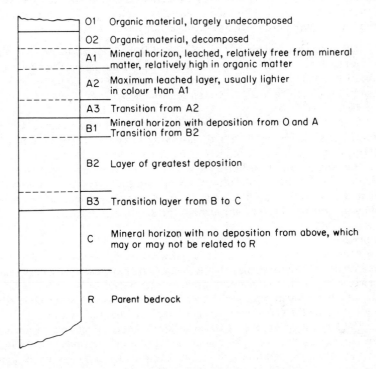

O1	Organic material, largely undecomposed
O2	Organic material, decomposed
A1	Mineral horizon, leached, relatively free from mineral matter, relatively high in organic matter
A2	Maximum leached layer, usually lighter in colour than A1
A3	Transition from A2
B1	Mineral horizon with deposition from O and A Transition from B2
B2	Layer of greatest deposition
B3	Transition layer from B to C
C	Mineral horizon with no deposition from above, which may or may not be related to R
R	Parent bedrock

Figure 4.3 A schematic diagram of a soil profile (see page 104)

O   The organic horizon, the layer formed above mineral soils by the breakdown of organic matter derived from plant and animal remains.
A   The mineral horizon nearest to the surface, subjected to the maximum leaching. Because of this the A horizon is known as the *eluviated* layer.

B   In this horizon deposition from the layers above has occurred, and it is referred to as the *illuviated* layer.

C   A mineral horizon different from A and B in that it is less weathered and relatively undeveloped. This horizon has not been affected by biological activity and it is not necessarily related to the underlying R horizon.

R   This horizon consists of the predominant underlying bed rock from which the higher horizons have originated, or with transported soils it may be unrelated to them. Thus it may be solid sandstone, granite or limestone giving rise to related horizons above or it may be a bed rock on which glacial or alluvial material has been deposited.

In addition to the letter designation described above, a main horizon that is waterlogged is indicated by the letter G, originating from the word *gley* or *glei*, which is often used to indicate a waterlogged horizon that has evolved under the influence of excessive moisture.

The successive horizons O, A, B, C and R may not all be present. For example, when a high water table has prevailed during profile evolution, the B horizon may not be present; or in areas of low rainfall where no significant leaching had taken place, the B horizon would not have evolved.

Each of the main horizons defined above is subdivided (figure 4.3) to form a system for defining and classifying successive layers in a profile. When land is cultivated, ploughing or digging changes the appearance of the O, A and possibly B horizons, unless the O layers are deeper than the depth of cultivation. The cultivations mix up the layers and, although at first the horizons may be simply inverted, subsequent cultivations make the soil more homogenous throughout the depth of cultivation.

Drainage

Examination of a field soil as a growth medium should include an assessment of drainage, particularly to evaluate how readily drainage takes place. A soil with a satisfactory drainage rate is said to be 'free draining', the depth of which may vary according to the seasonal water table (the level at which the soil is normally saturated) and the soil's texture.

The amount of water in a soil will have a direct effect on aeration and this in turn will affect the colour changes which normally occur in a profile. When the aeration rate is reduced, as under anaerobic conditions, the red and brown colours of the soil become paler; when aeration is virtually absent, these colours become grey or blue. These colour changes take place because the anaerobic bacteria reduce the brown and yellow ferric hydroxides to ferrous hydroxides, which are very pale grey or blue. The ferric hydroxides are practically insoluble, whereas the ferrous compounds are soluble and therefore mobile. Thus the ferrous compounds which are produced in a wet soil move in solution and are redeposited if the soil dries, causing a mottled horizon or even hard deposits of ferric hydroxides. This state is often referred to as *impeded drainage.*

Examination of the profile of a soil in the field will usually indicate how efficient the drainage is throughout the year. Soils that are uniform in colour, or have a gradual colour change down the profile, will normally be well drained ones. Drainage may vary, even over a relatively small area, and for a satisfactory assessment of the drainage characteristics of a particular field or area a minimum of ten borings per hectare should be made.

The factors of cultural origin that affect drainage are discussed in chapter 5.

Soil texture

Feeling the texture of a soil gives a good guide to its physical characteristics. When a moist sample is rubbed between fingers and thumb, an assessment can be made of the presence of sand, silt, clay and organic matter; usually only the first three of these, however, are easily felt because the humus content is relatively low.

Sand imparts the grittiness which may be felt when handling a soil sample. The actual particle size may vary according to the sand's origin (particle size has been referred to on page 00). Generally, the higher the proportion of sand in a soil the lower the cohesion, which may be thought of as the force that resists the breaking down of the soil into smaller particles by implements.

Silt imparts a silky or soapy feeling. A silty soil will not feel sticky but will have some cohesive properties.

All moist clays feel sticky and are cohesive when worked between fingers and thumbs; they also impart a polished feel.

Organic matter is very variable in size and origin; generally it feels soft and has cohesive properties.

Field assessments of soils

Soils may be classified according to the proportions of sand, silt, clay and organic matter that is thought or shown to be present (see table 4.1).

This classification allows for the variation that occurs in soils and is widely used by soil scientists and advisors in Britain and some other countries. Some experience of classifying soils according to texture is required before confidence is gained and the student is advised to take every opportunity to handle moist soil samples.

The textural classification of soils used by the US Soil Survey is shown in figure 4.4. The determination is made by mechanical means after the removal of organic matter and the soil classified according to the percentages of clay, silt and sand present.

Soil structure

Whereas natural soils ultimately consist of primary particles of sand, silt,

Table 4.1

Classification of soils according to composition

	Textural type	Examples
(1)	Sandy soils†	
	sand	coarse, fine or very fine
(2)	Loamy soils†	
	sandy loam	coarse, fine or very fine sand
	loam	
	silty loam	
	sandy clay loam	
	clay loam	
	silty clay loam	
(3)	Clay soils†	
	sandy clay	
	silty clay	
	clay	
(4)	Peaty soils	
	peaty sandy loam	
	peaty loam	
	sandy peat	
	loamy peat	
	peat	

† Organic matter may occur in these types, but where organic material is predominant the soils are classified as peaty.

clay and organic matter, these particles do not exist as independent distinct entities but form more or less stable soil crumbs or aggregates. The size distribution, shape and stability of these secondary aggregates is referred to as *soil structure*. Soil structure is one of the factors that determines the pore size distribution of a soil. Ideally, for horticultural purposes, a soil system with many well distributed wide pores is required, because these enable drainage to occur and provide aeration for plant growth.

When horticulturists refer to a 'good tilth' they mean a satisfactory soil structure that will enable cultural operations, such as sowing and planting, to be done with reasonable expectation of subsequent seedling or plant development, provided that water, nutrients and microclimate are adequate. The effects of some common practices to produce a satisfactory tilth are discussed in chapter 5. Once a good tilth is achieved, it is best preserved by minimal cultivation and traffic. Unnecessary cultivation will break the soil down to its basic constituents and when dry it will lose its 'structure' and become dusty.

In addition to mechanical cultivation there are other factors that

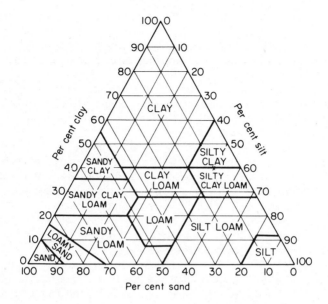

Figure 4.4 Composition of the soils textural classes as used by the United States soil survey.
The sand, silt and clay particle sizes are defined on page 00.

contribute to changes in soil structure. *Weathering* aids the formation of drainage channels and crumb structure: for example, when a soil dries during dry summer weather, water can drain through cracks or fissures, forming channels, which usually persist for the subsequent winter despite the contraction of vertical channels when the soil swells after being rewetted. The weathering of clods by freezing and thawing, or by alternate wetting and drying, plays an important role in the formation of drainage channels. The growth and death of plant roots produces channels and some roots help to form aggregates by growing into small existing spaces between soil particles and forcing them apart.

The burrowing activities of earthworms, moles, mice and other microfauna produce useful drainage channels. In addition, the soil that has passed through the guts of earthworms contains well-mixed mineral and organic materials; worm 'casts' greatly enhance the formation of the upper horizons of virgin soils, particularly in temperate climates.

In the culture of sports turf and ornamental lawns the worm casts are often regarded as a nuisance and measures are sometimes taken to control earthworms. Whether or not this is done, the use of spikes or hollow tines to produce vertical channels in the profile simulates the production of drainage channels by earthworms.

Grass crops greatly improve soil structure and when short term 'leys' are sown on arable areas the subsequent arable crops usually benefit considerably (see page 119). The longer term 'grassing down' of orchards (page 119) ensures that soil structure is maintained and improved, which is particularly important in temperate climates to prevent fruit trees from becoming waterlogged during the winter.

The difference in water infiltration rate between arable and grassland is illustrated by the fact that on any similar soil type, irrigation water can be applied to grassland at about double the rate at which it will start to damage arable land.

The addition of organic materials to soils other than peats improves their structure. As decomposition takes place the organic products help to bind the soil particles into aggregates. It is now generally accepted that some of the products (for example, polysaccharides) are adsorbed on to soil particles and so help to stabilize existing pores. There is also evidence that lipids present in soil organic matter can waterproof, and so stabilize crumb structure. The breakdown products of decomposing roots have the same stabilizing effect in the rhizosphere.

Many of the soils used for horticultural crops are naturally well-draining ones, but in others artificial drainage has been necessary to prevent waterlogging. Once a soil is drained satisfactorily, the factors described above will gradually improve its structure and enable it to be worked during the wetter months of the year. The condition of soils in the autumn is particularly important now that mechanical harvesting of crops such as potatoes and carrots is possible.

The collapse of soil pores and structure can result from misuse of machinery, from heavy rain and from faulty irrigation — for example, the use of too large water droplets. These cause the flaking or slaking of individual soil constituents from sides of the pores, which ultimately block them and reduce porosity.

Deflocculation of clay particles will cause a breakdown of aggregates containing clay, but the flocculation of such soils can be assisted by liming (see page 127).

4.2 CONTAINER MEDIA

When a plant is grown in a container its roots are growing in a restricted or confined volume of medium, and both the root system and its supporting growth medium are isolated from the adjacent environment.

The range of containers used for plant production is extensive and includes those for individual plants such as clay, plastic and peat pots, and those for several plants, such as boxes (or flats), and beds with sides and bottoms that cannot be penetrated by plant roots (for example, concrete carnation beds, polythene-lined troughs and beds on benches).

Most field soils are physically unsuited for container production because the frequent irrigation to which the soil in a container is usually subjected results in *panning*; plants then suffer from poor drainage which leads to waterlogging and insufficient aeration in the root area. Poor drainage is particularly serious in containers that are not porous, whether individual pots or large troughs. Under normal field conditions a given soil will drain to a lower moisture content than when it is containerized, because the container bottom will act as a barrier. Porous plant containers have a higher total evapotranspiration rate than others because of the additional water loss from the container surface, which is very large in relation to the volume of soil. Nevertheless container media should have a larger percentage of wide pores than field soils generally have.

A wide range of materials suitable for container media has been explored and the basic types are described later in this chapter. The main visual characteristic of artificially mixed media is that they are homogenous, and changes in profile do not occur as in a field soil that has evolved *in situ*.

A containerized plant can be easily moved from one place to another with the minimum of root disturbance, and planting can take place with minimal damage to the plant's root system. Horticulturists rely on this lack of disturbance and maintenance of the 'root ball' to enhance growth. The glasshouse industry uses containers for the production of many crops (for example, in the propagation of lettuce, cucumber, tomato and bedding plants) and nursery stock producers and garden centres offer containerized stock, such as conifers, deciduous trees and shrubs for planting throughout the year.

In addition to the advantages of mobility each plant in a batch of plants in individual containers has the same volume of medium available, so that within practical limitations uniformity of the rhizosphere is assured. This obviates the competition for nutrients and water that occurs when the root systems of several plants occupy the same medium.

Many of the media used in containers are free from weeds, either because the materials used, for example vermiculite, are manufactured or because of partial sterilization of (for example) the loam in John Innes composts by chemicals or steam to control weed seeds and perennating organs such as the rhizomes of *Agropyron repens* (Couch Grass).

Requirements of satisfactory media

There is a wide range of media available to the grower but a final decision on choice of a specific one frequently depends on economic factors such as availability and price.

Four requirements must be met for satisfactory plant growth to occur.

(1)   Mechanical support is discussed fully elsewhere (see reading list), but the reader is reminded of the practical requirements of anchorage and support. In addition, many glasshouse crops (for example, cucumbers and carnations) are supported by elaborate aerial systems.

(2)   The need for water is fully discussed in other volumes, but because
       the plant normally obtains its water from the medium in which its
       roots are growing, it is obvious that the medium must be able to
       retain water and make it available to the plant. The soluble salt level
       should not normally inhibit water uptake.

(3)   Oxygen is vital for root respiration and the root medium must have
       sufficient porosity for free air movement, allowing interchange of
       oxygen and carbon dioxide between the air and the root.

(4)   The nutrients required by a plant during growth and development
       must be present in the medium. This is usually achieved by
       incorporating the appropriate materials during preparation by
       subsequent liquid feeding or top dressing the medium, and
       occasionally by foliar feeding. In practice, plants produced in
       containers receive their nutrients by a combination of these
       methods.

Now that relatively inert materials are used in the preparation of
growth media, care must be taken to supply macro- and micro-nutrients.

Loam-based composts

For centuries growers have used a wide range of ingredients in container
media, often specifying a different compost for each genus or group of
plants.

In the 1930s workers at the John Innes Horticultural Institute in
England examined the requirements of plants that were containerized.
From their work emerged the John Innes Composts which were
specifications for both seed and potting composts based on formulations
using partially sterilized loam, peat and sand with suitable quantities of
base fertilizers added according to the estimated time that any given plant
would be in its container. Calcium carbonate was also included to maintain
a satisfactory pH and counteract the acidity of the fertilizers. A potting
compost suitable for calcifuges was formulated substituting ground
sulphur for the calcium carbonate.

The John Innes composts have been used, and still are to a lesser
extent, by commercial producers of many types of plants throughout the
world. There are several reasons for their decline in popularity. Firstly, the
commercial world is always under pressure from production costs, the
most important being the labour required to cut and stack suitable field
loam; the subsequent costs of preparation and satisfactory partial
steam-sterilization are high too. Many growers no longer have loam readily
available in their areas and transport costs have prohibited bringing
materials from afar.

Also, since the 1930s, when the original work on the loam-based
composts was done, progress has been made in understanding the nutrition
and management of other materials.

Loamless composts

The *loamless composts* are based on mixtures of peat and sand, or peat and processed mineral material such as vermiculite, or simply on peat only. Other materials (such as leaf mould) have been evaluated, their popularity often depending on local availability of ingredients.

Products of other industries are being tested: for example, in Britain the Forestry Commission is marketing chopped tree bark; in Denmark the use of rock wool (which is primarily produced as an insulating material) is rapidly increasing; and even chopped up plastic foam is used in some mixtures. All of these materials are relatively free from harmful organisms so it is not normally considered necessary to partially sterilize them before their use as commercial growth media. Most of them have a very low nutritional value compared with the loams used in traditional composts, so it is very important to ensure that macro- and micro-nutrients are included in the loamless compost mixes.

The loam or clay fractions in loam-based composts have high buffering capacities and some workers have suggested that peat and sand mixes should have some fine ground clay material added during preparation. The German compost *einheitserde* (meaning standardized soil) contains a mixture of peat and clay aggregates from a subsoil. As with other composts, nutrients are added but the clay fraction increases the buffering capacity of the compost.

The U.C. mixes

The University of California has developed composts based on mixtures of peat and sand, with the addition of suitable nutrients. The proportions of peat moss, fine sand and fertilizers may be varied according to the requirements of the species grown. The range of mixtures thus produced is large and in addition specifications are given that enable alternative materials such as rice hulls, redwood shavings or specific sawdusts to be used completely or partly in place of the peat.

It can be argued that the U.C. system offers commerce too wide a range of specifications, but it must be borne in mind that availability of materials varies from one place to another and that nurseries will wish to make the maximum use of local materials but at the same time ensure uniformity and repetition of satisfactory media.

The use of organic fertilizers such as hoof and horn, specified in the U.C. mixes and other composts, can lead to toxicity problems caused by free ammonia or excessive nitrites. These toxicities, which occur from time to time, are unpredictable and seem to be associated with rates of bacterial action in parts of the nitrogen cycle. There is a strong correlation with pH, phosphorus level and light, for the incidence of these particular toxicities is greater under the poor winter light or a high calcium carbonate content. Where levels of phosphorus are high the problem rarely occurs.

G.C.R.I. compost

The Glasshouse Crops Research Institute in England has guided the evolution of peat and sand-based composts further. Workers there have closely examined the toxicity and nutritional problems occurring during the use of peat and sand mixtures, and they have produced specifications that overcome these problems. First, materials such as hoof and horn have been replaced by slow-release urea-formaldehyde (see page 130) as a source of nitrogen, eliminating the risk of toxicities that originate from the decomposition of hoof and horn. Second, allowance has been made for the inclusion of nutrients such as boron, copper, iron, manganese, molybdenum and zinc by adding them in frits (see page 138).

Peat composts

Sphagnum moss peat-mixed with other materials has been used in growth media for a considerable time, but only in recent years has it been used alone as the basis of a substrate.

Peat, which is derived from *Sphagnum* and other allied moss species, is formed in certain areas of the world, particularly northern Europe, where the occurrence of the material is exploited (for example, in the Republic of Ireland, Finland and the U.S.S.R.

The natural pH of Sphagnum moss peat is normally between 3.7 and 4.0, and because of this low reading it was not considered as a satisfactory growth medium until recent years when the nutrition of plants growing in peat was closely examined. The addition of calcium carbonate or other suitable liming materials increases the pH enabling plants to make satisfactory growth. The nutrient level of a natural peat is extremely low, but all the necessary minerals can be included during preparation so that a perfectly balanced medium is produced.

Peat has a low bulk density. Thus its use reduces the weight of container media compared with more traditional mixtures containing loam or sand. There are several proprietary preparations of peat now available that contain all the nutrients required for satisfactory plant growth. As the peat is virtually sterile there is no need for partial sterilization and the incidence of soil-borne pests and pathogens is greatly reduced. As with other proprietary media the material can arrive on the nursery site in sealed bags ready for use.

Straw substrates

The technique of growing glasshouse crops on straw substrates has been developed mainly to overcome the problems of controlling pests and pathogens in the soil floor. Normally, where good control of the biological properties of the glasshouse soil can be achieved there is no merit in using the technique, but in commercial practice it is sometimes difficult to get satisfactory control when continually monocropping and it is uneconomic to change to alternative crops that are less susceptible to the prevalent disorders.

The technique of producing crops on straw substrates is usually successful for tomatoes, cucumbers and chrysanthemums, but a wider range of crops may also be grown. The principle is that baled straw that has started to decompose is used as the rhizosphere. Decomposition is initiated by saturating the straw with water and adding nitrogenous fertilizers. Bacterial action causes decomposition and initially there is a sharp rise of temperature up to $54°C$. The substrate is planted after the temperature has fallen below $38°C$ and is still falling. Some economy may be made by breaking the bales down into wads of straw before lining out in rows. A shallow layer of growth medium, such as a loam or peat compost, is put on the top, sufficiently deep for planting the container raised plants.

The rows of bales are isolated from the normal soil substrate of the glasshouse by polythene sheeting; the decomposed straw and polythene are discarded at the termination of each crop. Experience has shown that wheat straw is the most suitable of all the cereal straws, because it keeps its structural form longer. The loss of water from a straw-bale system is greater than from most other substrates, because evaporation takes place from the exposed surfaces; the water retention of the straw increases as the straw decomposes.

Another point of practical importance is the shrinkage resulting from the decomposition of the bales; allowance must be made for this when tying crops to overhead wires and support systems.

Carbon dioxide is produced during the decomposition of the straw and, as a supplement to the normal atmospheric level, it can be used in photosynthesis. The feeding of crops grown on straw substrates can be done through the normal irrigation systems in the liquid form. Additional nutrients to nitrogen are added to the bales after fermentation starts, according to the subsequent crop to be grown (see further reading list).

In the course of modern cereal production a wide range of persistant herbicides is used, making it necessary for the history of the straw to be determined before use. The straw should not be used when herbicides such as 2,3,6–TBA or Picloram have been used during the cereal production, because some glasshouse crops, especially tomatoes and cucumbers, are very susceptible to traces of certain growth-regulating substances.

SUMMARY

The horticultural potential of field soils may be assessed *in situ* by examining their profiles, which provide evidence of their origin, that is whether they have been formed as sedentary or transported soils. The effectiveness of the subsurface drainage may also be assessed. A mottled profile indicates poor drainage leading to anaerobic conditions. Soil profiles may be described according to their successive layers, or horizons. The top horizon is organic in origin, the next is a leached mineral layer, which contains some deposited organic material. Below this is a layer of mineral deposition, and then a horizon with no biological activity; this is less weathered and undeveloped; under this is the bed-rock horizon.

A useful determination of the soil's textural type can be made by feeling it with the fingers and classifying it as sandy, loamy, clay or peaty. Within these primary types there are intermediates such as sandy loam. Soils can also be classified from a laboratory mechanical analysis, which is based on the percentage of clay, silt and sand present.

Container growth media must provide mechanical support, retain water, be permeable to air to allow gaseous exchange, and retain nutrients for satisfactory plant growth. They are homogenous and should be more porous than field soils. The range of suitable materials is large but loam-based composts such as those developed at the John Innes Horticultural Institute have been widely used for many years. Recently mixtures of sand and peat or peat only have been used successfully provided that the necessary nutrients are added.

The problems of toxicities especially manganese toxicity, following the partial sterilization by steam of loams for composts has stimulated the adoption of loamless composts. The G.C.R.I. compost, which is based on sand and peat, includes a wide range of macro- and micro-nutrients.

Straw substrates have been developed in recent years and are particularly useful where it is necessary to isolate a crop such as tomatoes from an infected soil floor in glasshouses.

CHAPTER 5

THE MANAGEMENT OF SOILS FOR HORTICULTURAL CROPS

5.1 CONTROL OF PHYSICAL PROPERTIES

Cultivation

Any operation involving the soil, whether done mechanically or by hand can be regarded as a *cultivation*. Traditionally tasks such as ploughing, digging, seed-bed preparations and hoeing are included as cultivations. Whatever we do to or on a soil, whether or not in the presence of a crop, is likely to have some effect on the physical conditions of that soil. Possibly the effect is only temporary; on other occasions it may affect the physical structure for a long time. In this section some of the effects of different cultivation operations will be discussed.

Ploughing and digging

Both the *mouldboard plough* and the *spade* have evolved for the purpose of inverting the soil surface. It is accepted that both can be used for other purposes but here they are considered for their use for soil inversion, during which a solid moist mass is broken into clods and a soil that is loose breaks into smaller clods. In tropical areas, where smaller areas of land are cultivated by individual growers, the *draw hoe* is used in a chopping action to achieve the same effects.

The rough surfaces left from ploughing or digging increase the area exposed to weathering. Following winter digging, whenever soil temperatures are at or below freezing point, frost action may take place and the clods broken down into smaller particles. The effect of alternate wetting and drying is similar; the moist clods dry out and either shrink or crack. Any clay present will swell on re-wetting to produce more cracks, partly because of the uneven swelling and partly from absorbed air. In northern Europe and North America, for example, the winter weathering of ploughed or dug soils is relied on heavily as an integral part of their preparation. In areas that do not experience significant lowering of temperatures below freezing point the action of alternate wetting and drying is relied on for soil preparation.

During the course of ploughing or digging, materials such as weed canopy, crop debris or bulky manures are incorporated into the soil. Depth of ploughing or digging should be relative to the quantity of organic matter in the soil. The change from a darker to a lighter colour at a depth of about 30cm in most horticultural soils indicates that as the soil profile deepens the organic matter content decreases. There is normally no advantage in bringing the subsoil up to the surface because it normally lessens fertility. There is evidence that some of the shallow sandy soils are ploughed or dug too deeply. Where cultivations need to be deeper than the depth of the highly fertile topsoil, a *subsoiler* should be used rather than deeper ploughing. This ensures that only the soil containing most organic matter is inverted.

Harrowing and raking

These operations are intended to produce a tilth from the soil mass that has been previously ploughed or dug. The purpose is to provide a suitable physical environment for placement of seeds or young plants. Harrowing or raking at earlier stages may be used to incorporate fertilizers or other materials within the media.

Rolling

The process of rolling is sometimes used during final stages of preparation for extensive vegetable production prior to sowing or planting. The slight compaction resulting from rolling enables subsequent roots to be in close association with moisture-holding particles. Rolling is particularly beneficial on the lighter soils, since it reduces surface drying during germination and may also reduce the possibility of an organic soil blowing away before the crop canopy becomes established. The process of rolling should not be confused with a need to level or grade the surface of a given area, because unnecessary rolling may lead to detrimental compaction.

Rotovating

Rotovators are generally used in horticulture to produce a tilth. They are frequently used during the summer months in preparing for the next crop, particularly on market gardens where hand-steered machines are operated; in large-scale vegetable production rotovators are tractor mounted.

Unfortunately rotovation brings to the surface a lot of dormant weed seeds and care must be taken to ensure adequate weed control following its use. There is an increase in germination rate of some weed species associated with the use of rotovators; for example, more Annual Grass (*Poa annua*) and Groundsel (*Senecio vulgaris*) germinate after rotovating than after ploughing.

Cultivating and hoeing

The prime purpose of cultivating or hoeing during the growth of a crop or a mixed stand of plants is to control the weeds. The weeds compete with the cultivated plants particularly for soil moisture, nutrients and light. At one time it was thought advisable to maintain a loose tilth at the soil surface, but now the production of this layer is not only considered unnecessary but it leads to excessive loss of soil water by evaporation. Additionally, plant roots are damaged, particularly with shallow rooted plantation crops. Many growers now accept that where herbicides are available for the control of weeds present in a given crop, there is no need to cultivate. The implications of chemical weed control associated with soil physical conditions are discussed later.

Compaction

This is not a deliberate operation but frequently results from some of the other operations such as spraying and harvesting, in addition to ploughing and cultivating.

Compaction may be defined as the increase of the soil's dry bulk density resulting from the rapid application of a load; simultaneously there is a decrease in porosity without a change in the moisture content. In most instances compaction occurs as a direct result of using tractors and machinery on the land; it usually impedes root growth and reduces aeration and it is likely also to impede drainage.

The compaction that occurs is not always obvious on the surface of a soil. It may take place at the depth of ploughing, particularly when successive ploughings are to the same depth, and results in a plough pan. The term *pan* is used to denote some forms of compaction below the surface. The incidence of these forms of compaction may be reduced by varying the depth of ploughing from year to year or by using a subsoiler in conjunction with the plough. A subsoiler is an implement behind the plough share, which pierces the soil below the depth of the furrow; the subsoil is thereby loosened without bringing it to the surface.

Some compaction may also result from the tractor wheel that runs in the furrow. This could produce a pan over most of the area as a result of several years' ploughing. Taking heavy vehicles and machinery on the land when it is too wet will also cause compaction. With modern equipment it is possible to accomplish work despite wet soil, and frequently the scheduled cropping programme and high level of investment in machinery dictate that work proceeds despite poor soil conditions. The consequences are often a loss of soil structure which cannot be measured until the subsequent crop is growing or even harvested.

Rainfall and irrigation

A change in the physical condition of a soil surface may occur as the result of impact of heavy rain or droplets from irrigation. The impact of water droplets breaks down the soil surface aggregates, forming a *cap* or *crust*. Both the structural stability of the soil and the water-droplet size contribute to this cap formation. Generally, the larger the droplet size the greater the possibility of capping. The formation of a cap leads to interference with subsequent water penetration and gaseous exchange; there is less gaseous diffusion with a wet cap. A dry cap is a physical barrier to seedling emergence, although the experimental evidence with lettuce is that there is no significant difference in yield following cultivating to break the cap or leaving it intact. However, if a cap forms because of large droplets applied immediately after sowing, then a light raking two to five days after irrigating has been found to improve the seedling emergence.

Drainage

Excess water may enter the root zone of crops either from the surface as rain and irrigation water, or from the subsoil as a result of a rising water table. For most horticultural crops a relatively low water table of about one metre is desirable at most times of the year. If the water table is too high, the anchorage of bush and tree crops is affected. There are exceptions to this rule with fen peat soils where a high water table is tolerated and is encouraged for crops such as celery. In addition the higher water regimes reduce the oxidation rate of the peat. Some of the Netherlands glasshouse industry is situated on land with high water tables, but the level is maintained sufficiently low for crop production by pumping water from surrounding polders into larger drainage systems. This control over water level is very skilfully manipulated by Dutch growers.

If water originating from the surface does not drain away sufficiently fast, there is water logging and anaerobic conditions prevail. In less severe circumstances the soil is too wet for normal cultivations to take place.

Drainage problems also arise from compaction and other influences on physical conditions which make the soil impervious. It is frequently possible to improve surface drainage by improving soil structure, and planning cultural techniques which improve the pore spaces in a soil.

It may be necessary to remove water that percolates through a soil, in which case tile, plastic or mole drainage systems are planned to deal adequately with the subsurface water; this surplus water is passed into streams and rivers. The water content of a given soil can vary considerably from one season to another. The naturally earlier draining areas have been developed for horticultural crop production because they can be worked earlier in the year. The need for a subsurface drainage system is often apparent prior to the development of a permanent site for glasshouses, orchards or sports areas, in which case it is prudent to put down a drainage system at the outset.

Rotations and break crops

The use of rotations has been advocated for many years; it was originally thought that different successive crops could benefit one another, either because of the nutrient residues they left or because of the nullifying action of detrimental root toxins. More recent studies have revealed that growing the same crop continuously without added nutrients leads to an incremental decrease of yield. However, there is little doubt that the same crop can often be grown continuously provided that its nutrient requirements are supplied. In horticultural production there is little opportunity for integrating the grain crops in a rotation. This practice is probably the reason for the success of the traditional farming rotation. Nevertheless, there is some merit in rotation from the point of view of crop hygiene, particularly now that we have a better knowledge of the so-called replant diseases. The implications of monocropping are discussed on page 147. There is clearly a case for leys in vegetable production. Farmers use vegetables as break crops to prevent continuity, and in many instances these can be profitable cash crops. Unfortunately there are few break crops that horticulturists can use which will obviously increase or maintain income.

Leys

Occasionally growers and farmers grass down an area that has been under arable cultivation. The grass is normally down for about a year and may include other plants, such as clovers, sown as part of the mixture. The practice of *ley farming* is common where arable crop production is closely integrated with livestock. The system is also used in some extensive vegetable-producing areas, and is very beneficial in the long term because the grass plant remains significantly raise the organic matter content of the soil. Grazing by cattle or sheep ensures partial manuring of the site and the residues from nitrogen-fixing clovers are also an advantage. Sometimes hay or silage crops are taken from the field. When the ley is terminated it is normally ploughed in. Thus the soil organic-matter content is increased, the workability of the land is improved (particularly in a wet spring) and there is generally increased permeability especially in a clay soil. In a sandy soil the binding effect of the supplementary organic matter is an advantage. With crops that are susceptible to wireworm (*Agriotes* spp.), leatherjacket (*Tipula* spp.), or swift moth larvae (*Hepialus* spp.), care should be taken to provide appropriate insect control, since these soil pests tend to increase in grassland and may prove troublesome in vegetable crops following the leys.

Grassing down of orchards

In some respects this is a similar principle to leys, except that the grassing down is normally permanent once the decision is made to change an orchard soil area from clean cultivated to a sward. The method is to establish top fruit trees (such as apples and pears) in cultivated soil until they start to crop. When this stage is reached it is desirable to regulate the growth of the trees by undersowing with grass (or grass and clover mixture), whose sward competes with the trees for nitrogen. As a result fruit colour and storage quality improve. In some instances the natural wild grasses and flora are allowed to develop at the cessation of cultivation, and this is known in England as a *natural tumbledown*. Whatever the method of establishing the grass it is important that it be kept mown. Traditionally sheep or even cattle may be grazed in these areas, but with the introduction of less vigorous fruit-tree rootstocks less grazing is done, although in south-east England and northern France such traditional practices may still be seen. The grassing down of top fruit on a garden scale has obvious aesthetic advantages too. The grass improves soil structure, counteracts surface water run off, and moderates the nitrogen available to the fruit trees. Frequent spraying programmes are easier to accomplish when the area is grassed down than when fallow, and there is less likelihood of unnecessary compaction and surface smearing taking place when machinery operates in a grassed-down orchard.

Green manuring
The practice of sowing a short-term crop (such as lupins, vetches, mustard and rye grass), which is ploughed *in situ* while in full growth, is known as *green manuring*. It is a practice which has been used in agriculture and vegetable crop production in the past, but is not used so frequently now in horticulture. There is an obvious similarity between composting leys and green manuring, for in both the green crop is turned directly into the soil while still growing. The organic matter and nitrogen levels of the soil are increased and the formation of nitrogenous compounds by the green manure crop prevents leaching during a wet season. It is therefore of particular use in the tropics and sub-tropics where there may be substantial rainfall between cash crops. Green manuring is not likely to increase the humus content of a soil to the same extent that a grass ley does. It is also not considered to be of great overall benefit, partly because the green and immature tissue decomposes very rapidly and stimulates the soil organisms to decompose the existing soil humus. Thus there may be a nett loss as a result of green manuring. Also in dry areas the production of a crop for green manuring may use up vital soil water. It is important that green manuring be evaluated if it is considered in the programme of arable crop production. The operation must not interfere with the programmes of crop production, and the potential loss of a cash crop must be taken into account. Overall there is unlikely to be a place for green manuring in the future of temperate horticulture.

It has been shown that green manuring reduces the incidence of common scab (*Actinomyces scabies*) of potatoes where it is prevalent. This is thought to be because the green manure material encourages the growth of saprophytic forms of actinomyces, which suppress the pathogen.

Mulching
The materials and systems used for mulching vary considerably in different parts of the world. It is important when evaluating a mulch to define the actual material used. A mulch (probably derived from the German word *molsch* meaning soft, beginning to decay) can be any material which is applied to the surface of a growth medium with the intention of reducing water evaporation, suppressing weeds, modifying soil temperatures and

generally improving productivity. Many materials can be used to achieve any or all of these functions, such as organic manures, straw, leafmould, spent mushroom compost, peat, lawn mowings and other natural materials. In recent times interest has developed in the application of manufactured materials such as black polythene, paper, and metal foil. The pineapple plantations of Hawaii use a paper mulch, and the use of black polythene mulches has produced increased yields of outdoor crops of tomatoes, sweet corn and cucurbits.

Agricultural cereal producers in western Canada and parts of the United States use a technique referred to as *stubble mulching*. The essence of this is that after wheat has been harvested the stubble is left and the next crop is drilled directly into it. This reduces the possibility of soil erosion. The technique is hardly applicable to horticultural crop production but certainly could be considered when vegetables follow cereal areas susceptible to erosion.

The reasons why mulching is successful are complex. First, there is the effect on soil moisture. The loss of soil water by evaporation is reduced but entry of irrigation or rain water is not adversely affected when organic mulches are used. There is a reduction in the incidence of soil compaction from rain and irrigation water. In the long term the increased biological activity under a mulch leads to increases in the water infiltration rate, thereby reducing surface runoff and soil erosion. In areas of high evaporation a mulch will indirectly reduce the soluble-salt level that results from deposits of salts in the upper soil layer.

During the winter months the soil temperature under a mulch is higher than similar areas without mulches. Conversely, in summer the sub-mulch temperature is lower. This illustrates the overall insulating effect of mulches and probably indicates the value of the technique in areas of amenity horticulture, where liberal top dressings of materials such as leafmould are placed around choice plants in the autumn. It also indicates the purpose of using mulches, particularly in glasshouses where there are outbreaks of *Fusarium* spp., which are pathogens thriving under relatively high soil temperatures. Here soils are possibly insulated from solar gain and additionally a new root system may develop in a pathogen free area nearer the surface under the mulch.

The colour of the mulch will also have a great bearing on the increase of soil temperature. The coverage of the soil surface with black polythene can lead to earlier crops, although the increased value of the crop is not always in keeping with the cost of the material.

There is evidence that a surface organic mulch can increase the organic matter content of a soil more than ploughing in the same quantity. Certainly mulching affects the microbial populations; their activity increases partly because of the increased soil moisture and partly because of the greater quantity of organic materials in the surface 2.5 cm. On the other hand the organisms responsible for nitrification are less active, presumably because of the lower temperatures, and a transient shortage of nitrogen may occur following the use of some materials.

The effect on macroscopic fauna is significant. Their improved environment during winter in a temperate climate enables them to remain active in the top soil, and the increase in temperature reduces the risk of death, which may otherwise result from low temperatures. The overall effect of increased earthworm activity is a more stable aggregate in the top 20 cm. In tropical soils termites probably play the same biological role as the earthworms do in temperate areas. The digestion of a mulch is more rapid but the same improvement of tilth and water percolation rates have been observed. This overall improvement of soil fertility promotes root activity in the surface layers. There is also an improvement in soil aggregation. The chemicals from fresh plant residues are leached into the soil, but the quantity of these leached nutrients from fresh materials can be very significant particularly with large quantities of rain or irrigation water passing through. It has been suggested that the organic acids from natural mulches increase the availability of soil phosphorus and prevent the formation of iron or aluminium phosphates.

The fairly constant moisture regime under a mulch avoids the fixation of potassium that would occur under fluctuating regimes; there is an increase therefore in the available potassium.

There are the so-called *yellow lungu* soils in Uganda, which are naturally very acid with low levels of exchangeable base. These conditions increase the available manganese and thus crops grown on these areas are very likely to take up toxic quantities of manganese.

Heavy mulches are used in the production of some crops in the glasshouse industry. In the production of roses under glass a 20 cm mulch of bulky organic manure is put on each year. In addition to the many advantages outlined above, the natural fermentation process produces carbon dioxide. This is a useful addition to the glasshouse atmosphere and increases the rate of photosynthesis.

In the tropics weeds are sometimes encouraged, so that they may be cut down from time to time to form a mulch. The overall effect is to aid the entry of water into the soil and avoid excessive surface runoff. It also reduces the compacting effect of tropical rains.

The choice and use of a mulch will depend on local availability and cost of suitable materials. The main purposes and advantages of mulching plants in a given situation should be considered before making a decision.

It is possible that some adverse side effects will occur with some mulching materials; composts and bulky organic manures may contain weed seeds or perennial organs which have not been killed in processing; nematodes and other pests may also be introduced from infected plant debris. Materials such as straw may bring about a temporary nitrogen deficiency.

Noncultivation systems

With the advent of herbicides the concept of crop production in a weed-free environment has become realistic. With arable vegetable crops this has led to studies and practice of closer spacings aimed at greater crop production with increased uniformity. Use of herbicides to control weeds has led to reduced management costs because of the reduction in time and labour spent in traditional hoeing and cultivating.

In addition to these obvious management advantages of noncultivation systems there have been increases in overall soil fertility and a greater stability of soil physical conditions. There has been some surface crusting, particularly in plantation crops, but this has not had a significant adverse effect on physical conditions or crop yield. The overall water infiltration rate has been improved, although not on sloping sites: in these situations a combination of chemical weed control with surface mulches could be advantageous. There is a tendency for crops to have root development nearer the surface in the absence of cultivations and roots are therefore in an area of higher nutrient status. The formation of a surface crust in these circumstances is not likely to be detrimental. Some workers have reported that there is less tendency to frost damage where there is no disturbance of the soil surface. The mechanical harvesting of arable crops, particularly roots and tubers, is easier where the formation of clods and compaction have not occurred.

There are claims that yield reductions occur with the use of chemical herbicides. This is indeed possible but it is more likely to be a direct effect of the chemicals on the crop plant than an effect on the overall soil fertility. The minimum of herbicide to control the weeds should be used, and as dormant weed-seed populations decrease following the use of herbicides, the dosage can be reduced in subsequent seasons to minimise the possibility of adverse effect on the crop.

There are many modifications available for the normal arable cropping. Each is designed to aid management, improve soil fertility or to increase yield and quality of crop production. Many of these techniques are just as applicable to amenity areas as to commercial ones. Mulching with natural materials may well be better management than frequent hoeings which are costly and lead to unnecessary loss of water.

5.2   CONTROL OF CHEMICAL PROPERTIES

Crop nutrition

In horticultural crop production the same attention is not paid to nutrient levels in the end product as is given by agriculturists producing crops for animal feed. An agriculturist will be very aware of the importance of magnesium in animal husbandry and will ensure that there is sufficient available in the grassland to avoid magnesium deficiency in the livestock.

It could be argued that horticulturists should be just as aware of the nutrient requirements of the consumer in addition to the crops' requirements, but it must be borne in mind that the animal that consumes grass and roots on the dairy farm is confimed to the same environment and diet for most or all of its life; the human consumer of horticultural crops, on the other hand, has a varied diet and is unlikely to eat fruit and vegetables produced on the same holding for the whole of his lifetime. Nevertheless the food-processing industry and retail outlet companies with high levels of quality control may call for high nutritive values as well as other qualities in horticultural products. All the experimental work on nutrition of vegetable and fruit crops tends to be directed at increased yield and quality. There is very little experimental work done on the nutrition of ornamental plants except where there is a saleable end product.

The student, grower and adviser will frequently read results of nutrient trials on different crops, and while some information will be of general use and interest, some of it will be very specific and largely applicable to the conditions under which the described experimentation was done. The results may only be a guide to expectations in another situation. A natural corollary of this is for growers to conduct their own nutrition trials. The results of these could be misleading in the hands of the layman because the planning, layout, recording and general conduct of this work should be done by trained persons using statistical techniques. However, with the tendency for horticultural enterprises to get larger by amalgamations, cooperatives and other factors aimed at increasing the viability of individual holdings, the concept of evolutionary experimentation becomes possible. Evolutionary techniques in horticulture imply that the best treatments from an experiment are taken forward into the next year and repeated with slight modification to other factors that may be interacting.

The chemical elements with which we are concerned in crop nutrition are normally classed in two groups, known as the *macro* (or major) and *micro* (or trace) *elements*.

Macronutrients (major nutrients)
These are carbon, hydrogen, oxygen, nitrogen, sulphur, phosphorus, calcium, magnesium and potassium. The plant obtains the first three from the photosynthesis of carbon dioxide and water.

Micro nutrients (trace nutrients)
The micronutrients are boron, iron, zinc, copper and molybdenum. There is some speculation about chlorine but there is probably insufficient evidence to include it at this stage.

These two groups are not designated to denote the relative importance of the elements in plant nutrition but to indicate the relative proportion of each that is required for satisfactory growth.

It is possible to get a maximum response to the application of a given quantity of a known fertilizer; this does not imply that maximum yield for that crop has been reached. First, the response from one nutrient in a fertilizer interacting with additions of another nutrient must be examined and the ultimate response related simultaneously to a given set of environmental conditions.

There is no easy solution to finding the optimum nutrient regimes for crop production because conditions such as day length and temperature are always changing. We have to use our knowledge, which is continuously increasing as the result of new experiences and experimentation, to produce the maximum yields of optimum quality crops in a given situation.

The horticulturist makes preparations, which ensure that the soil or growth medium is in the best possible physical, chemical and biological state for the proposed crop. He is soon aware of the extensive interaction which is going on between these three factors. From the plant nutrient point of view, the preparation should include (if necessary) the adjustment of pH and the addition of sufficient organic materials or fertilizers for the nutrient requirements of the crop, at least for the initial stages. Ideally, these applications will be based on the results of a soil analysis, which should take into account problems that are characteristic of the site and which may not be revealed by the standard analysis.

The current concept of crop production is to work according to a predetermined programme. This works well with some glasshouse crops where there is good environmental control and a wealth of research results indicating the best conditions for different growth phases. The glasshouse tomato crop can be produced according to a cultural programme, which specifies temperatures and nutrient regimes according to the stages of growth. There are obvious difficulties with outdoor crops but progress is being made to produce workable programmes with these as well.

In addition to base dressings nutrient requirements during subsequent growth and development should be considered. It may be necessary to change the ratio of nutrients available during growth; for example, during the life of a glasshouse tomato crop it is normal practice to liquid feed from about the fifth leaf stage with a nitrogen to potassium ratio of 1:2. However, when the plants have fruit ripening and developing on about five fruit trusses, there is a general tendency for the plant to be less vigorous. This can be counteracted by changing to a 1:1 nitrogen to potassium ratio. With outdoor vegetable crops or fruit plantations top dressing with materials containing nitrogen or potassium fertilizers may be required. With brassica crops such as sprouting broccoli and spring cabbages which are planted out in the late summer or autumn and overwintered, relatively low levels of nitrogen are given before the winter, but heavy dressings are given in the spring to encourage an increase in leaf size. If these dressings were given in the autumn and early winter, soft large-celled tissue — which is frost-susceptible — would be encouraged.

Early summer cauliflowers are planted out in March or April and once they are established a readily soluble inorganic fertilizer such as potassium nitrate may be applied. Black currant is an example of a fruit crop which responds to high levels of nitrogen applied in the spring.

Regular soil analysis will ensure that the nutrients are maintained at optimum levels. It does not always follow that what shows up on analysis as available in the soil is actually entering the plant, for there may be *nutrient antagonisms*. In recent years techniques of leaf or tissue analysis have been developed. These results can be extremely useful provided we know what the optimum nutrient levels (referred to as *index levels*) in the plant should be for particular times of the year or cultural conditions. When these index levels are known, satisfactory comparisons can be made but it is very important that samples be taken from tissues of similar age and situation to the index. Some nutrients are very mobile within the plant and haphazard sampling will produce very misleading results.

Tissue analysis also provides an ideal technique for diagnosing micronutrient disorders. It is possible for nutrient deficiences to occur before symptoms are seen on the plant; in these cases potential nutrient deficiences may be corrected before yield is affected.

Nomenclature of fertilizers
Crop production has been increased and improved for a long time and many growers are traditional in their terminology. Many people still use the old fashioned style of naming chemicals; for example, ammonium sulphate and potassium chloride are known as sulphate of ammonia and muriate of potash respectively. Here the current chemical name is used partly for scientific accuracy and partly to promote the use of correct nomenclature, particularly in a world where there is increasing interchange of information and common names differ from place to place.

Sources of nutrients
There are many inorganic and organic materials used in crop nutrition. The organic materials listed in this text are given as examples of the relatively common materials available in most parts of the world at the present time. The bulkier and commonly used concentrated organic materials are discussed under the organic additives later in this chapter.

Legislation and percentage content
Most countries have legislated for the nutrient contents to be stated when a fertilizer is sold. It has been, and still is for some elements, customary to express the plant nutrient as the oxide; for example, potassium as potassium oxide K_2O, which was commonly called potash, and phosphorus as phosphoric acid P_2O_5.

In this section on nutrients both the elemental percentage, and the oxide percentage, where still used, are given. The astute student of chemistry will notice that the percentage stated does not always correspond with the percentage expected of the pure compound. The reason for this is that many fertilizer materials contain impurities, which although often useful nutrients themselves, reduce the percentage content of the main nutrients. In such cases the cost of a higher purification level of chemicals used as fertilizers would be prohibitive.

Liming
The importance of the pH of growth media has been explained in earlier chapters and is referred to again later in relation to availability of nutrients. One of .the objects of liming is to increase the pH of the medium, possibly with the intention of making available nutrients that are unavailable at lower pH levels. In a peat-based medium lime is required to raise the pH and to provide calcium as a nutrient. Phosphates, in the presence of large amounts of iron or aluminium, form less soluble compounds in acid conditions than in alkaline conditions, so there may be an induced phosphorus deficiency if there is a low pH. The solubility of manganese and aluminium compounds increases in acid soils thus producing levels of either of them which could become toxic to susceptible crops. Calcium carbonate is included in soil-based composts to counteract the acidity from the other base fertilizers which are included as nutrients.

In addition to the chemical effects mentioned above, lime has the physical effect on clays of increasing flocculation and thereby improving soil structure.

The importance of calcium in plants
Calcium is necessary for the growth of meristems and ensures the satisfactory growth of root tips. Calcium pectate plays an important role in the formation of the middle lamellae of plant cells. Calcium possibly plays an important part in the absorption of nitrogen, and calcium bases neutralize organic acids in the plant.

Calcium deficiency symptoms in plants
Plants with a deficiency of calcium have smaller root systems and leaves; calcium is not mobilised in the plant so the younger leaf tissues are first to show symptoms.

Some plant pathogens are sensitive to pH; Clubroot, caused by *Plasmodiophora brassicae*, is discouraged at the higher pH levels. A pH of 6.5 to 7.0 is therefore desirable for brassica crops, and if this disease occurs it may be an indication of a lowering of pH. The disorder of tomatoes called blossom end rot is sometimes caused by lack of available calcium; on the other hand, common scab of potatoes (*Actinomyces scabies*) is discouraged at lower pH levels.

Liming materials and control of pH

Growers are advised to have regular assessments made of pH of soils and growth media by competent analysts. This practice will ensure that early indications of a lowering of pH come to their notice before problems arise. The presence of weeds that are calcifuges such as spurry (*Spergula arvensis*) and sorrel (*Rumex acetosella*) indicate a low pH. Heavy dressing of lime may be necessary in the reclamation of acid areas. For most crops the object is to bring up the pH to 6.5 or 7.0, but this does not apply to calcifuges such as ericas and rhododendrons, which are grown commercially or in amenity plantings. The finer grasses desirable in an ornamental lawn are encouraged by a lower pH than that preferred by the coarser grasses, so it is inadvisable to use liming materials in the preparation of a lawn.

There are several liming materials available for horticultural use:

> *calcium carbonate,* occurring as limestone, chalk or marine animal deposits;
> *calcium oxide,* commonly called burnt-lime or quicklime;
> *calcium hydroxide,* commonly called hydrated or slaked lime.

There are also liming materials that supply magnesium in addition to calcium; the most important ones are:

> *magnesium carbonate,* commonly called dolomitic limestone;
> *magnesium and calcium oxide mixtures,* sold as burnt magnesium lime;
> *magnesium hydroxide and calcium hydroxide mixtures,* sold as slaked magnesium lime.

No liming material is pure and some useful micro-nutrients including manganese, zinc, and molybdenum are added to soils when large quantities of lime are used.

The role of nutrients in plant growth and their application

Nitrogen

Plants take up nitrogen either as the nitrate or ammonium ion. It is believed that the nitrate taken up by the plant is reduced to ammonium before further synthesis by an enzyme containing molybdenum (manganese also plays a role in the reduction). The ammonium ions are utilized in the synthesis of amino acids and proteins, resulting in a larger amount of leaf tissue. Horticulturists use this principle when applying top dressings of quick-acting nitrogenous fertilizers to increase growth of brassicas and other crops, where more leaf tissue is desirable, or to improve the appearance of ornamental lawns. In the presence of high levels of nitrogen in the plant, the ratio of cell protoplasm to cell-wall material tends to produce leaf tissues with large, but relatively thin-walled cells (see also the importance of calcium page 127). In the production of leafy vegetable and salad crops this may be desirable from the consumer's point of view and also to some extent in relation to increased productivity of crops. However, the larger-celled tissues have a higher water content; excessive nitrogen therefore results in the so-called *soft growth* which is more susceptible to frost, desiccation and pathogens and pests which attack foliage. In temperate climates it is not normal practice to give plants top dressings of nitrognous fertilizers immediately before the winter period, but to use suitable quick-acting materials in the spring.

Plants suffering from nitrogen deficiency show the symptoms mainly in older leaves and tend to be smaller than normal; leaves are smaller in size and paler in colour. There is a tendency for leaves to age prematurely, and deciduous trees have an earlier leaf fall. Apple fruits are smaller and highly coloured with good keeping quality.

Nitrogen fertilizers
Ammonium sulphate (21 per cent N) is used in conjunction with some other fertilizers, but should not be mixed with materials containing free lime because ammonia will be evolved, leading to loss of the material and possible scorching of plant tissues. Ammonium sulphate reacts with calcium carbonate in the soil; the sulphate materials will tend to produce acid conditions, although not where calcareous materials are predominant such as in soils derived from limestone.

Ammonium nitrate is available for use in liquid feeds. It is inflammable and therefore is not often formulated on its own. There are manufacturers who mix it with limestone and prepare a granular mixture. *Nitrochalk* is such a material; it contains 15.5 per cent N. The calcium materials present counteract the effects of the acid characteristics of the ammonium radicle.

Urea (46 per cent N) is normally used as the nitrogen compound of liquid feeds. It may also be used where a very quick-acting nitrogenous fertilizer is required, as on ornamental lawns and for foliar feeding of lettuce.

Potassium nitrate (12-14 per cent N and 37 per cent K) is particularly useful in liquid feeds, because it contains both nitrogen and potassium.

There are two forms of ammonia used as liquid fertilizers in crop production:

anydrous ammonia (82 per cent N)
aqueous ammonia (20—30 per cent N)

Their application requires specialized equipment and the work is normally undertaken by contractors. The use and application of these materials has been pioneered on agricultural grasslands and cereals, and subsequently evaluated for other arable crops. Liquid nitrogen fertilizers are particularly useful on crops which have a large nitrogen requirement in the spring and have a relatively long growing period. Recent work has shown that injecting ammonia to a depth of 12.5 cm (well below sowing depth) at a rate up to 336 kg/ha does not damage crops that are row spaced. Done in the spring this technique avoids leaching and is particularly suitable for use on leeks 10 weeks after drilling, and Brussels sprouts eight weeks after drilling the seed.

Slow-release nitrogen fertilizers release nitrogen at a steady rate due either to a slow rate of dissolution or to breakdown by microbial activity. The nitrogenous fertilizers previously mentioned dissolve in soil water relatively quickly. It was thought that the slow-release nitrogenous fertilizers would be of general use in horticulture, but their high unit cost has tended to exclude them from use in extensive production where the normal water-soluble nitrogen fertilizers are still preferred. Following the development of peat and other composts for the glasshouse industry the slow-release materials have become widely used. The materials that are generally available are:

Urea—formaldehyde resins
Casein } waste products from the plastic industry,
Formalized casein }
Isobutylidene diurea (IBDU), available in different granule sizes to provide for different rates of release,
Osmocote, a membrane resin-coated material,
Magnesium ammonium phosphate (Mag Amp).

The traditional slow-release nitrogenous material used in composts is hoof and horn, but toxicity from ammonia or nitrite may occur, particularly if there is a high lime content in the compost.

In composts based on peat there is a very low population of nitrifying bacteria. If the rate of decomposition is too slow, there may be a shortage of nitrogen in the early stages and this would be particularly harmful to a fast-growing and quickly maturing crop.

Experimental work has indicated that IBDU, casein and Mag Amp, and to a lesser extent Osmocote have release curves correlating with the absorption of nutrients by short season crops. As more consideration is given to the application of nitrogen and other nutrients by liquid feeding systems, the demand for slow-release nitrogen materials suitable for container media may decline.

Phosphorus
Phosphorus is found in nucleic acids, nucleotides and phospholipids and also plays a vital role in plant metabolism. This element is important for the development and growth of roots, particularly in the early stages of plant life. Phosphorus is likely to become unavailable in the soil because of its fixation into insoluble phosphates of aluminium and iron. In acid soils the water-soluble phosphorus fertilizers (for example, monocalcium and ammonium phosphates) form insoluble precipitates with iron and aluminium. Applying the fertilizers to the soil in bands or as granules will reduce the chances of nutrients becoming unavailable in this way, because

there is less contact between the fertilizer particles and the soil. There is also a higher phosphate concentration in the soil solution around the fertilizer granule. The chemical aspects of phosphate fixation are discussed in chapter 3.

Phosphorus deficiency symptoms are very similar to those caused by nitrogen deficiency, but the outstanding difference is that plants deficient in phosphorus develop a bluish green leaf colour, which later turns purple.

Phosphorus fertilizers
Superphosphate (9 per cent P) is a mixture of monocalcium phosphate and calcium sulphate. It should be applied during cultivation to a soil which has adequate lime. The monocalcium phosphate is converted to di-calcium phosphate, which is soluble in the soil solution. If the soil has excess free lime the insoluble tri-calcium phosphate is formed. Under acid conditions the calcium phosphates combine with iron or aluminium compounds to form insoluble phosphates.

Triple superphosphate (20 per cent *P*) is a mono-calcium phosphate and has more than double the phosphorus value of superphosphate.

Basic slag (4.5 to 9.5 per cent P) also contains lime, 25 to 35 per cent calcium and small amounts of other nutrients, of which magnesium and manganese are particularly useful. Other nutrients that are found in this material include iron, copper, molybdenum, zinc and boron. Basic slag is known in some countries as 'Thomas slag'. This is complimentary to S.G. Thomas (a British metallurgist) who developed the use of a tip retort for separating phosphorus from pig iron. The fertilizer is generally used in base dressings during soil preparation. It is available in granular form to facilitate spreading.

In addition to the phosphatic fertilizers discussed above there are:

Monoammonium phosphate (12 per cent N and 26 per cent P);
Dicalcium phosphate (usually 23 per cent P);
Diammonium phosphate (21 per cent N and 23 per cent P).

These materials are rarely applied as straight fertilizers but are mainly used in the preparation of compound fertilizer (see page 137).

Potassium
This is the most abundant cation in plants; it acts as an osmotic regulator; it is essential for the synthesis of chlorophyll, proteins, carbohydrates and fats; and is an important contributor to enzyme activity. There is evidence that satisfactory levels of potassium must be present in the leaf for optimal photosynthesis rates.

Potassium is generally considered by horticulturists to be necessary for the satisfactory production of fruit, legumes and flower crops. This is probably to ensure production of optimum yields in the presence of relatively high levels of nitrogen and phosphorus. Together these three nutrients assure high cropping potentials. It is generally accepted, for example, that the ideal ratio of available nitrogen and phosphorus and potassium in the media for tomatoes should be 1:1:2. For leaf crops the ratio may be 1:1:1.

Potassium is very mobile in the plant. It can be applied to counteract excessive response to nitrogen, but high levels of available potassium in the growth medium can induce deficiency of magnesium in the plant. This is because of so-called ionic antagonism, which occurs in growth media containing high levels of potassium and insufficient magnesium ions in solution. (This is especially so with crops such as glasshouse tomatoes where large quantities of potassium fertilizers are given). The ionic antagonism may be counteracted by base dressings, which include magnesium sulphate, and in the short term by foliar sprays of magnesium sulphate.

Leaves of potash-deficient plants become bluish green, often with marginal scorch.

Potassium fertilizers
Potassium chloride (about 50 per cent K) is used widely as a source of potassium. The chloride radical tends to build up in the soil when this fertilizer is used at high rates; in the glasshouse industry this is avoided by the use of potassium sulphate. Soft fruit (for example, strawberries and raspberries) are adversely affected by the residues of chloride left in the soil.

Potassium sulphate (about 42 per cent K) is favoured as a supply of potassium in the production of high-value glasshouse and vegetable crops. In cost of nutrient related to the material it is more expensive than potassium chloride.

Potassium nitrate (about 13 per cent N 36 per cent K) is mainly used in the preparation of liquid feeds.

Materials from flues contain potassium, but the content varies according to the process producing the ash. (There is the possibility of some toxic elements being present with ashes from some other sources). The ash of burnt seaweed, which is often referred to as *kelp*, may have a relatively high potassium level but it is very variable according to source. Private gardens may use bonfire ash as a nutrient source to advantage: the potassium content varies widely according to the origin of materials prior to combustion, but values of between 2 and 5 per cent potassium may be expected. Because of the high solubility of the ash residues they should be spread while fresh.

Magnesium
Magnesium is a constituent of the chlorophyll molecule and is also the activator for several enzymes in the metabolism of the plant. There is evidence that magnesium is essential for the mobility of phosphorus within

the plant; thus there is a complementary action of increasing a plant's phosphorus content by ensuring that there is adequate magnesium available. As mentioned in the section about potassium (page 132), relatively high levels of available potassium can result in magnesium-deficiency symptoms in the plant. These are generally a loss of the green colour between the veins in the older leaves and a yellow to dark coloured necrosis follows if severe. In brassicas red or purple coloured leaves occur. Autumn tints are particularly noticeable in many deficient plants.

Magnesium fertilizers

Magnesium sulphate (9.7 per cent Mg as $MgSO_4 7H_2O$), commonly known as Epsom salts, is used to increase magnesium levels where a relatively high magnesium requirement is indicated. It can be included in base dressings to supply magnesium and to increase soluble salt level as required in glasshouse crop production (particularly for tomatoes). Magnesium sulphate may also be applied as a foliar spray. *Kieserite* (16 per cent Mg as $MgSO_4.H_2O$) is not as readily soluble as magnesium sulphate and is normally used in base dressings where magnesium application is indicated. It is used by glasshouse growers to raise the soluble salt levels.

Some materials contain magnesium in addition to other elements: Basic slag (page 131) contains variable amounts of magnesium up to 7 per cent Mg; dolomitic limestone (page 128) (10–12 per cent Mg) is particularly useful where it is necessary to apply magnesium to acid sandy soils; burnt magnesium lime (about 6 per cent Mg) contains both magnesium oxide and calcium oxide.

Sulphur

Sulphur is a plant nutrient that has not had a great deal of attention in Western Europe, although interest in this element's effects on plant growth is increasing. Sulphur is a constituent of many plant proteins and is also contained in the oils present in brassica seeds. Legumes require relatively high amounts of sulphur. Sulphur deficiences have been identified in several parts of the world including Australia, New Zealand, North America and Africa.

When sulphur is added to soil, weak sulphuric acid is formed leading to a lowering of the pH; sulphur dressings are therefore used in amenity work when a lower pH is required. As sulphur is not mobile within the plant, symptons show first in the apical growth as uniformly yellow or chlorotic leaf blades which sometimes have a purple tinge. Citrus fruit trees and cotton plants are particularly susceptible.

Sulphur fertilizers

The amount of sulphur in rain is often sufficient to supply crop needs; this sulphur originates from the combustion of hydrocarbon fuels. It has been calculated that the annual quantity of sulphur in rain amounts to 12 kilogrammes of sulphur per hectare (approximately 10.8 pounds per acre); areas nearer to industrial centres may receive a larger quantity. The use of sulphur-containing pesticides is now declining because more sophisticated materials are available.

There are many common fertilizers that supply sulphur; for example, *ammonium sulphate* contains about 24 per cent S, *magnesium sulphate* (13 per cent S) and *potassium sulphate* (17.5 per cent S). In areas where extra sulphur is required, additional to that contained in the examples cited above, *calcium sulphate* (18.6 per cent S) may be used; this compound is commonly called *gypsum*. The development of compound fertilizers (page 137) has led to the use of materials with little or no sulphur in their molecules, but elemental sulphur may be incorporated in the granules or coated onto them during manufacture.

Micronutrients
The levels of micronutrients in normal and healthy plants are considerably lower than those of macronutrients. For example, both boron and zinc occur in healthy apple leaves at between 25 and 50 parts per million measured from the dry matter content. As has already been pointed out the micronutrients are just as essential to healthy plant growth as the macronutrients.

The availability of micronutrients for plants from their growth media is somewhat varied according to origin. Cultivated soils that have developed on sedimentary formations usually have adequate supplies, but the range of soil-less media used for the root environment has increased in recent times and adequate micronutrients may not always be present.

Bulky organic materials and crop residues will return some micronutrients to the production area. Many micronutrients are distributed as impurities in irrigation water, rainfall or other fertilizers. Even pesticides can provide a supply of certain micronutrients; for example, growers who use *maneb* (a manganese dithiocarbamate fungicide) are applying manganese. Furthermore, the weathering of geological materials will maintain a supply of some micronutrients in natural soils.

It is possible that the increased productivity from more intensive growing methods causes deficiencies that would not normally have occurred. The use of inorganic fertilizers is not adversely criticized here, but it is possible that the traditional methods of nutrition, which used organic fertilizers, supplied sufficient micronutrients for the crop production systems used.

It is important to anticipate micronutrient disorders, identify them when they occur and counteract them quickly and accurately.

Iron
This micronutrient is present in the enzyme that takes part in the production of chlorophyll and is also necessary for photosynthesis.

Iron deficiency occurs frequently on calcareous soils and is often referred to as *lime-induced chlorosis*. Occasionally an imbalance of other macronutrients is responsible for a similar chlorosis. Iron-deficiency symptoms may occur with potassium deficiency or by excess of available phosphorus. An unusual iron deficiency occurs in the Mendips, where the dolomitic limestone has a high zinc level. Iron deficiency may also occur following prolonged use of sewage sludges, which are rich in zinc.

Generally, iron-deficiency symptoms are a reduced concentration of chlorophyll, which results in the typical 'chlorosis', usually associated with terminal shoots. Individual leaves of affected plants show interveinal chlorosis and there is a marked reduction in growth rate. Citrus trees that have iron deficiency are unable to mature all the fruit set.

The deficiency frequently occurs in glasshouse crops as a result of unhealthy roots. Whereas a foliar application may have a temporary remedial effect, control of pathogens in the root environment may be a more successful answer in the long term.

To control iron deficiency in fruit trees, foliar sprays of ferrous sulphate (a 5 per cent solution) at the rate of 400 litres per hectare are often successful. The technique of placing tablets of ferrous sulphate in the trunk tissues has also been used successfully.

Chelates (or sequestrating agents) are often used in the control of iron deficiency; chelates are organic compounds that coordinate metal ions very strongly because there is more than one point of attachment of the organic molecule to the cation. The metallic nutrient will therefore not precipitate and subsequently becomes unavailable in the soil. Ethylene-diamine tetraacetic acid (EDTA) is the sequestering material most frequently used. As well as iron sequestrene there are other metallic micronutrients available in this form, including copper, manganese and zinc.

Manganese

This element is present in enzymes responsible for respiration. It is also important in chlorophyll synthesis, because deficiencies of manganese affect chloroplasts. It is thought that manganese is an oxidizing agent, with the role in the plant of reducing ferric iron to ferrous iron. Thus, if there is excess of manganese, symptoms of iron deficiency will occur in the leaves because the ferric iron is not able to be used. Manganese deficiency is most likely to occur in alkaline soils because the greater the acidity of a soil the greater the manganese availability.

The symptoms of manganese deficiency are pale chlorotic leaves. The pale areas are interveinal with veins remaining dark green. It is often visually difficult to differentiate between manganese and iron deficiency symptoms.

A disease of peas sometimes occurring in Britain (commonly called *marsh spot*) is caused by manganese deficiency. It gets its name because the deficiency occurs on the Romney Marsh in Kent. In apparently otherwise healthy pea plants a brown spot develops on the cotyledons of the peas in the pods. The application of manganese sulphate as a foliar spray is the quickest method of correction, but base or top dressings of manganese sulphate can be made.

Zinc
This element occurs in an enzyme involved in cell oxidation and regulates the use of sugars. It plays an important part in changing carbohydrates from one form to another. Zinc is a component of the enzyme that catalyses the decomposition of carbon dioxide and water; it is also important in the natural synthesis of tryptophane which in turn is involved with the formation of the hormone indoleacetic acid.

Deficiencies of this element are rarely found in European soils, but frequently occur in the crops of fruits and nuts in North America, where it is sometimes correlated with the inability to form extensive root systems. This is especially so in soils that are mechanically difficult for roots to penetrate. The deficiency symptoms are generally associated with the problems of auxin synthesis in affected plants. For example, pecan shoots form rosettes, and other trees produce small leaves. This condition is known as *little leaf*, and is particularly characteristic of citrus, peach and other fruits with zinc deficiency.

To control zinc deficiency in plantation crops the growing of a cover crop (such as lucerne) or allowing weeds to grow before cutting them down, enables the more efficient root systems of these herbaceous plants to take up the zinc; the element is thus returned to the soil via the organic matter of the cover-crop debris.

Sprays of zinc sulphate can correct the deficiency in trees, but for arable crops it is better to include zinc sulphate in the base dressing.

Copper
Copper is present in some of the oxidising enzymes of the plant cell. Many plants that have tissues in stems and fruits that darken on being damaged or cut contain tyrosinase oxidases; these include tea, beans and artichokes. The tyrosinases are an important group of protein enzymes.

In addition to the importance of copper in the plant, this element has a vital role in the soil because it is connected with the precipitation or inactivation of certain toxins present in the soil. Growth media with high organic contents sometimes present problems because of their low copper content. This phenomenon was noticed in the 1920s on reclaimed land in Holland.

Copper-deficiency symptoms in citrus-fruit trees appear as *die back* of shoots, and there is a tendency for the fruit to fall prematurely. In other top fruits there is shoot die back, chlorosis and premature leaf fall.

To control copper deficiency the careful application of copper sulphate either as a soil dressing or foliar spray has been used. Many fungicides contain copper and their use in prevention and control of plant pathogens has probably led to sufficient copper being available in situations where deficiences may otherwise occur.

Molybdenum

Molybdenum is present in the enzymes that enable plants to change absorbed nitrate to nitrite and ammonia. This element is also vital for the fixation of nitrogen by the nodule-forming plants. In addition it is involved in the synthesis of ascorbic acid and for counteracting excessive amounts of copper, boron, manganese and zinc.

Molybdenum-deficient plants display chlorosis, particularly mottled chlorosis. This is followed by marginal curling, wilting and, later, necrosis and leaf wither. The symptoms occur first in the older leaves. In the cauliflower, deficiency of molybdenum is responsible for the condition called whiptail, the symptoms of which are a reduction of the leaf laminae, and in severe cases the loss of the growing point resulting in 'blindness'.

Molybdenum is more available under alkaline conditions than acid, thus liming will improve the situation where the deficiency occurs. Sodium molybdate can be applied as a soil dressing or foliar spray to correct the deficiency. Sufficient of the element can be given to brassicas in the seed beds before planting out to last through their life. Techniques for applying sodium molybdate with insecticidal root drenches to prevent cabbage root fly have been developed.

Boron

This element plays an important role in the uptake and use of calcium within the plant. It is thought that calcium is necessary for protein metabolism, pectin synthesis and other vital processes (such as maintaining water relationships within the plant). Despite the present lack of knowledge of the total function of boron there is no doubt as to its importance.

Boron-deficiency symptoms differ greatly from one crop to another. They include *brown heart* (or raan) of turnips and swedes, *hollow stem* in brassicas, particularly cauliflower, also *browning* of cauliflower curds, *internal corky core* in apples, *die back* and *cracked fruit* of peaches.

Boronated fertilizers are available for use where boron deficiences are likely to occur although their use unjustifiably is not recommended; care must be taken to spread them evenly. Borax (sodium tetraborate) is used in some liquid feed systems to maintain the element for some glasshouse florist crops, especially carnations.

Compound fertilizers

In recent years mixtures of nutrients have been marketed. The term *compound* is used in the United Kingdom and some other countries, whereas in America the term *mixed fertilizers* is preferred.

Compound fertilizers are formulated and expressed as ratios of nitrogen, phosphorus and potassium, and are produced in combinations of any two or three. Because of the legislation currently in force the nutrients sold in the United Kingdom state the ratio as $N : P_2O_5 : K_2O$, although this is abbreviated to $N : P : K$. Some of the micronutrients may be included; for instance, boron for use where boron deficiency is likely to occur.

Having the fertilizers compounded in the factory normally ensures correct proportions and thorough mixing. The preparations are easy to store and handle. Usually they are produced in granular form, which has several advantages: gradual release; facility of spreading, especially in windy weather; and reduction of the likelihood of materials settling on and scorching plants following top dressing. The fertilizer manufacturers produce compounds for all commercial crops and for general use. Some of them are referred to as *concentrated fertilizers* because compounds with nutrient value in both anions and cations are used in the manufacturing process, as with monoammonium phosphate, diammonium phosphate and dicalcium phosphate.

Frits

To ensure slow release of micronutrients in growth media and water culture, preparations are made of finely ground glass containing the nutrients. When used in growth media they slowly break down releasing the nutrients over a long period of time. Different frits are available containing one or several minerals. The availability of micronutrients in soilless composts is ensured by inclusion of the appropriate frits in the mixture. In the culture of watercress zinc frit is used to control crook-root fungus.

Fertilizer placement

Interest has been aroused over the last few years regarding the ideal positioning of fertilizers in relation to the plant. This was particularly stimulated (1) by the fact that phosphorus can become unavailable when it forms insoluble compounds in the soil, (2) by the loss of some nutrients by leaching, and (3) by the need to obtain the maximum returns for the investment in fertilizers. Some fertilizers, particularly those containing nitrogen or potassium, when placed adjacent to seeds will increase the soil's osmotic pressure, thereby reducing germination and emergence of the seedlings. Fertilizers containing phosphorus do not generally have this effect, and for many years gardeners have placed either superphosphate or basic slag in the bottom of seed drills to ensure adequate supplies of phosphorus for young plant development. With the advent and increased use of compound fertilizers it is not possible to differentiate between the placement of different nutrients.

Combined seed and fertilizer drills allow accurate placement and experiments indicate that with most vegetable crops placement of the fertilizer 50 mm to the side of and 25 mm below the seed gives good results.

Placement of fertilizers allows better utilization of limited resources, and with an increasing concern in some parts of the world about the excessive use of fertilizers a fuller study of the subject could lead to smaller applications.

Liquid feeding

This technique is the application of plant nutrients in solution, systems for which are well developed in the glasshouse industry. Normally the distribution is through the irrigation system, particularly when this is at a low level in relation to the plant. It is possible to distribute nutrients through overhead systems but this could lead to uneven distribution, especially where the plants are in small containers.

Distribution systems of the drip or trickle type are available, allowing each plant to have its own liquid feed outlet. This type of system is very commonly used in the production of glasshouse tomatoes, cucumbers and pot chrysanthemums. In outside cropping more growers are applying nutrients through the irrigation spraylines. Nursery stock, particularly when in containers, and high-value vegetables are fed in this manner.

There is a high level of control of nutrient input in well-designed systems. Normally a dilutor, working on the *venturi principle* holds the stock solution. A better alternative is based on an injection system, whereby a known quantity of stock solution is injected into the distribution water. The stock solution contains the nutrient concentrate, which is a solution of the required nutrients before their dilution in the distribution system. Chemical fertilizers that are frequently used in making liquid feeds are *urea, potassium nitrate* and *ammonium nitrate*. Frequently a nontoxic vegetable dye is put in the stock solution to aid identification and to give an indication of the concentration of nutrients in the irrigation water. It is normally possible to vary the dilution rate, either manually or automatically, depending on the sophistication of the system. The dilution rate in relation to the stock solution is very important, because this is the key to the control of what the plants are receiving. Ideally, dilution rates received at the soil by the plants should be referred to in parts per million for each nutrient. But often growers only know the dilution rate of say 1 in 250, and do not know what the plants are actually receiving. Liquid feeding can be very accurate; give a very even distribution of nutrients; save considerable time in the nursery; and be flexible to enable nutrients and their ratios to be modified according to season and crop requirements.

Tablet feeding

This is a relatively new technique developed in the United States and

Australia. It is suitable for plant-growing in containers, particularly hardy nursery stock. A tablet of highly compressed nutrients, usually based on urea-formaldehyde, potassium and phosphorus compounds, and micro-nutrients is placed on the surface of the growth medium. The initial watering disintegrates the tablet and the force of the next watering spreads the mixture over the surface of the container medium, where nutrients are slowly released. Tablets of various size and nutrient ratios are formulated to provide suitable nutrient regimes for a period of three to four months.

The advantages of such a system are that all other nutrition could be dispensed with and treatment with a tablet before leaving the nursery would ensure sufficient nutrient available for the period in the retailer's garden centre. The system also lends itself to flowering and foliage plants sold through the florist trade.

Control of soluble-salt level

In glasshouse production there is a very high level of investment in controlling the environment. This induces the need to obtain maximum crop yields. One obvious limitation on yield would be inadequate nutrients, and glasshouse growers normally practise high levels of crop nutrition. Some fertilizers leave residues in the media and, because they increase the soluble-salt level, the osmotic pressure of the solution in the region of the root is high and it becomes increasingly difficult for plants to extract water. Subsequently the plant's growth is restricted, but this is an asset with some crops; tomatoes, for example, produce higher quality fruit when grown in a soluble salt concentration of 2800 micromhos, but at higher concentrations the restriction is excessive and growth is unnecessarily restricted to the detriment of the crop. In a crop where free growth is encouraged (for example, *Asparagus plumosus*) the soluble-salt level is kept very low.

The skilful grower will manipulate soluble-salt level according to crop requirements, by adjusting the levels in conjunction with base dressings and subsequent feeding. Adjustments can be made to liquid feeds and if they reach too high a level clear water can be given to leach out the salts.

Desalinization

In arid conditions there are circumstances where water rises from below, and high evaporation rates make the salt level of the soil too high for satisfactory crop growth. Ideally irrigation with water of relatively low salt content will improve the situation by lowering the soluble salt level. Some irrigation waters contain high salt levels and can only be used in limited quantity, alternatively, irrigation water can be desalinated by a suitable process.

If sea-water flooding occurs, the sodium chloride introduced will upset the cation-exchange system. This is because the sodium ions displace other ions (such as calcium), which are absorbed on the colloidal particles. The subsequent sodium complex is not satisfactory for normal cropping until reclamation is complete. The initial objective of reclamation is to leach out the excessive sodium chloride solution and then the soil is dressed with calcium sulphate (gypsum). The calcium ions displace the absorbed sodium ions which subsequently leach out leaving a reinstated calcium clay humus complex (see also chapter 3).

5.3 MAINTENANCE OF PHYSICAL PROPERTIES

The need for maintaining the physical composition of growth media has been discussed in previous chapters. The different methods of achieving this in practice will be evaluated here.

In broad terms there are two classes of materials that can be applied to soils to maintain or improve their physical properties, *organic* and *mineral*. Each plays a vital part in maintaining soil fertility. In practice it is unusual to apply mineral materials on a field scale purely to improve physical conditions, partly because of economics and partly because there is a tendency to accept the mineral content of a field soil and cultivate and crop it accordingly. However, when choosing sites for protected cropping, factors such as winter light intensity are of prime importance and soil factors tend to take second place. Therefore, following the erection of protected structures a fairly high investment may need to be made to improve the soil, and large quantities of materials such as peat may be used. Additionally, because of the large quantities of irrigation water applied during growing seasons and for soaking following partial sterilization by steam, it is sometimes necessary to pay attention to the mineral content of a glasshouse soil as well as to increasing its level of organic matter present.

Organic additives

With the increased use of inorganic fertilizers less emphasis has been put on organic manures as a source of nutrients, and this has led to a decline in the addition of organic materials to soils. Another factor is the scarcity and rising cost of organic manures. The stage has now been reached of trying to determine whether or not there are advantages in the use of organic manures additional to their nutrient value. It is anticipated that more research will be done to find the answer to the question of whether the fertility of soils is declining because insufficient organic matter is added during current cultural practices. The functions of organic matter in a medium have been outlined in chapters 1 and 4, and if we accept that the soil is a complex environment, which requires a balance between organic and inorganic materials, then we must accept that the maintenance of a certain minimum organic level is necessary. Additionally, soils with good physical characters lend themselves to the vigorous cropping programmes that are now used in the horticultural industry, in that they allow mechanized operations to take place over a longer period of the year than soils with poorer physical qualities.

Organic additives are discussed below from the point of view of increasing the organic content of a soil. The student should consult further texts for detailed nutrient contents of the organic manures.

Crop residues

It is customary in some growing regimes to return the crop remains to the cultivated area. The possibility of leaving crop residues *in situ* depends very much on the crop and its method of harvest. The ploughing in of root crops and remains of brassicas are examples of this practice. The remains may be either foliage or root debris and vary tremendously from one part of the world to another. Some crop remains are available once they have been processed by the industries using horticultural products; spent hops from the brewing industry are a good example. Private gardeners have long recognised the value of this material when inorganic fertilizers have been added. It is not possible to put either nutrient or monetary value on these crop residues, since the cost of transport and handling must be allowed for, and the range and availability of the material varies greatly from one area to another.

Straw is an agricultural crop residue that is fairly readily available, particularly where the growing of horticultural crops is integrated with cereals. It is ploughed in or sometimes composted, but there seems to be no real advantage in composting if allowance is made for the initial demands on nitrogen by soil bacteria and the straw is of manageable length. Chopping up the straw will facilitate ploughing in, and the addition of a suitable nitrogenous fertilizer will ensure that there is no temporary nitrogen deficiency (when using ammonium sulphate for this purpose the weight ratio of chemical to dry straw should be 1:20). If the straw is ploughed in during the winter, half of the nitrogenous fertilizer should be applied in the spring to avoid loss by leaching. In areas of poor drainage or where the water table rises during the winter months to give anaerobic conditions, decomposition is not likely to take place.

Farmyard manure (F.Y.M.)

This is the classical organic material used in maintaining and improving soil fertility. It is produced in most parts of the world where animal stock are housed and consists of straw or other bedding material mixed with animal faeces and urine. Its nutrient content varies with the nutrition of the animals, for poorly fed animals will produce manure that is low in plant nutrients. The average mineral composition of farmyard manure is given in table 5.1. The values were obtained from fifty samples collected from a wide range of farms in the West of Scotland. All the samples were partly rotted and considered to be in a suitable state for spreading.

It must be emphasized that these nutrient figures are averages. Nitrogen

Table 5.1

Mean composition of fifty samples of farmyard manure †

Element	Content in dry matter,	Supplied by 10 tons F.Y.M. (20 per cent dry matter)
	per cent	cwt
N	1.73	3.46 $(NH_4)_2SO_4$
P	0.24	1.20 Superphosphate $(18\%P_2O_5)$
K	1.29	1.30 Muriate of potash
Ca	0.74	0.74 $CaCO_3$
Mg	0.34	0.68 $MgSO_4$
	ppm	oz
Mn	182	52.3 $MnSO_4.4H_2O$
B	23.5	14.7 $Na_2B_4O_7.10H_2O$
Cu	19.8	5.6 $CuSO_4.5H_2O$
Co	1.66	0.56 $CoSO_4.7H_2O$
Mo	2.32	0.46 $Na_2MoO_4.2H_2O$

† After figures given in reference 2 for this chapter.

varied from 0.52 to 3.47 per cent and 5 per cent of the samples contained less than the equivalent of 50 kg of ammonium sulphate for a 10-tonne dressing. As it is generally accepted that less than 30 per cent of the total nitrogen is utilized by crops in the first year, dressings of inorganic fertilizer should be included in the base dressings. The phosphorus and potassium levels were lower than generally believed. On the other hand, figures in the table show the mean value of 3.4 per cent magnesium to be equivalent to 84 kg per hectare (0.68 cwt per acre) of anhydrous magnesium sulphate. This amount is a useful nutrient contribution in crop production. The figures given in the table for the trace elements indicate that F.Y.M. is a useful source of these essential nutrients.

Such analysis figures for bulky organic manures make it not surprising that inorganic fertilizers produce satisfactory crop growth when compared with materials such as F.Y.M. The need to maintain the applications of inorganic fertilizers following dressings of F.Y.M. has been demonstrated on peaty fenland soils growing celery, although normally for most crops inorganic fertilizers should be used only to redress the deficiencies of the F.Y.M. The use of inorganics alone supplies no humus to mineral soils, nor are the other micronutrients necessarily given. Despite this latter point it could be claimed that under good management with accurate and prompt diagnosis it is preferable to apply foliar solutions to correct micronutrient deficiencies. The plant nutrient content of F.Y.M. is heterogeneous and its composition variable according to animal origin, proportions of straw, water content (the dry matter content is only about 20 per cent), age and storage conditions.

Poultry manure
This material is available in Europe and North America where poultry are housed intensively. As with F.Y.M. the nutrient content of poultry manure can vary considerably, with the organic matter content at about 20 per cent. Some of the nitrogen is present as undigested food and the remainder (about 70 per cent) is of urinary origin, which is made up of 60 per cent uric acid and 10 per cent ammonium compounds. When stored, particularly under wet conditions, the uric acid present changes to urea and ammonium compounds; if the manure heats up, then ammonium salts volatilize off. Thus it is recommended to spread the fresh material on to the fallow soil surface and mix in. Rain will wash nitrogen and ammonium compounds into the soil, where they will be converted to nitrates by soil bacteria. The soil should remain fallow for two or three weeks during this process to avoid ammonia scorch of plants.

Miscellaneous natural organic manures
There is a wide range which includes materials such as guano of bird or fish origin; the so-called slaughterhouse waste materials which include dried blood, meat and bone meal, hoof and horn; and waste products such as wool shoddy. These are all useful fertilizers according to their analysis, but because of the relatively small quantities used per unit area they do not contribute significantly to the organic matter content in terms of soil structure. Some of them have been much coveted by horticulturists in the past. For example dried blood (usually containing 14 per cent nitrogen) has been used by market gardeners and amenity horticulturists as a relatively quick-release nitrogenous material.

Sewage sludge
This is primarily a nitrogenous organic material. The dried sludge contains approximately 3.0 per cent nitrogen and 0.5 per cent phosphorus; its potassium level is extremely low at less than 0.2 per cent. Care must be taken not to apply sewage sludges too frequently; otherwise there may be a build up of some metallic residues (for example, zinc or copper compounds are often present in relatively high proportions). It is not possible to generalize about the toxic materials that may accumulate from the continued use of sewage sludges, since they will depend on the industrial and other processes occurring in the catchment area of the sewage before processing.

Compost
A wide range of plant and animal debris can be decomposed prior to their being applied to soils as bulky organic materials. The composition of these composts will vary considerably according to initial material used, additives and methods of storage.
    The composting of plant refuse has been widely practised by private

gardeners who maintain good soil fertility by adding these humus-forming materials to their soils. Most garden refuse can be used; lawn mowings are particularly useful, and it is probably because of the large ratio of mown lawn to cultivated areas that the compost heap has been so successful in European private gardens. Either calcium cyanamide, ammonium sulphate or other suitable nitrogenous accelerators are added to assist decomposition by microbial action. Composting is not widely practised on a commercial scale; the use of straw as a source of compost material is quite possible, although there is little merit in this compared with ploughing in the undecomposed straw. However, some vegetable producers find it convenient to produce straw compost and stand the material in heaps for a few weeks, during which time it is turned and damped. The ratio of fertilizer to compost for encouraging nitrifying bacteria is 1:10 by weight of nitrochalk per ton of dry matter.

With more attention being focused on the enviroment and the effects of disposal of waste materials, it is likely that more municipal authorities will produce composts of selected materials suitable for horticultural purposes: such materials are often referred to as *town refuse*. It is important that toxic contaminants and diseased material are excluded in the preparation of composts; there is also the likelihood of glass, ceramics, metals and plastics being present which will not break down and these should be removed before processing.

Mineral additives

Materials in this class are used where there are problems of drainage in the top soil or where physical conditions are difficult to maintain by using organic matter only. It is unlikely that any of these mineral additives would be used on an extensive scale, but they certainly have their place in the protected cropping industry and amenity horticulture where physical adjustments to natural soils are required (see page 141). Mineral materials in the form of coarse aggregates are added to soils to increase their porosity and are of particular benefit where sharper drainage is necessary. Coarse sands, perlite, calcined clay, cinders and other coarse aggregates may be used in commerce. Granite and limestone chippings are the materials most frequently used in northern Europe. Other mineral additives are river-bed gravels and pulverized fuel ashes. Choice of suitable material should be correlated with cost and availability, but due consideration must also be given to the possible effect on pH. In the glasshouse industry, where it is difficult to keep the pH up to 6.5 or above, limestone materials are preferred. In the Channel Islands granite chippings and alkaline gravels are available so glasshouse growers are able to choose an appropriate material according to the pH. In amenity horticulture chippings are used as a surface mulch for alpine subjects: in addition to the aesthetic appearance of such mulches due consideration should be given to the maintenance of a suitable pH for the plant subject. Thus limestone materials are more suitable for calcicoles, whereas granite chippings (particularly those of acidic volcanic origin) are preferable for calcifuges.

Chemical additives

Several natural and synthetic chemical soil conditioners are being evaluated at the present time; although some of these have apparently improved soil structure, increases in crop yield have not always been reported. When 'krilium' (sodium polyacrilonitrile) is applied to soils, it stabilizes crumbs for a period of two years and increases soil aeration by increasing total pore space (see page 23). There are several natural and synthetic rubber latex preparations that stabilize surface aggregates; similarly, bitumen emulsions are used. One of the effects of these materials is to stabilize existing surface structures, and when applied after soil preparation but prior to seed sowing, both germination and subsequent young plant growth are improved. Chemical and mineral conditioners or additives are useful in counteracting the soil-surface capping that results from irrigation or heavy rain.

5.4 CONTROL OF BIOLOGICAL PROPERTIES

Range of organisms in growth media

The biological spectrum of a growth medium may include a wide range of organisms whose diversification applies to size and phylum.

Within a given growth medium we may find evidence of bacteria, actinomycetes, protozoa, fungi, algae, insects, mites and nematodes, as well as the more familiar macroscopic organisms such as earthworms. Complex media such as field soils, which have evolved naturally, will usually contain this entire range. Materials that are mined or manufactured (for example, vermiculite or rock wool) will not normally contain these organisms, particularly prior to use for plant growth, although many of them will subsequently invade the medium. In a strawbale substrate for example, bacteria are relatively inactive at the outset but cultural techniques encourage the development of those that participate in the nitrogen cycle.

This concept may be applied to most growth media used in plant production so we need to look a little closer at this aspect of media although lack of space precludes a full discussion of soil biology. Scientists generally agree that the crop plants, the pathogens and pests, and the soil microflora and fauna that form the rhizosphere have a mutual effect on each other. This is represented in figure 5.1. The soil microflora and fauna and soil-borne plant pathogens and pests are relatively quiescent until stimulated by other biological activity. From the horticultural point of view they are activated by root exudates and decomposable residues from the crop plants. Our knowledge of the processes in parts of this diagrammatic representation is greater than in others, and we need to find out more regarding the interactions between the microflora and soil-borne plant pathogens.

Undesirable biological constituents

There are systems where the same crop is produced in successive seasons; for example, glasshouse tomatoes are mainly in the hands of specialists who grow this crop annually, and chrysanthemums may be produced all the year round. In the nursery stock industry the same areas may be monocropped continuously and a parallel situation exists with perennial

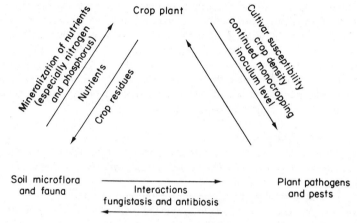

Figure 5.1 Diagrammatic representation of the ecological equilibrium between the crop plant, plant pathogens, and soil microflora. Factors between the arrows are two way while other factors exert influence in the directions indicated.

fruit and with production on the same site of plantation crops. When any of these forms of monocropping is practised, there is an increased possibility that plant pathogens and pests will accumulate. Large populations of undesirable eelworms or pathogens have led to a condition often referred to in the past as 'soil sickness'. This term is rather vague because it implies that there has been a diminution of soil nutrients as well as other changes. The fact that continuous monocropping has led to a build up of eelworms is not necessarily implied, although we now see this condition as an eelworm problem, particularly when virus-transmitting nematodes are involved. Thus an imbalance of biological properties is frequently the cause of decline in productivity and it is better to be more specific than referring to the problem as 'soil sickness'.

Now that more is understood about the free-living eelworms that are capable of transmitting plant viruses, the term 'specific replant disease' has come into use particularly when referring to a specific eelworm population affecting a given crop species.

Methods of control

When evaluating a problem and deciding on a course of action, both the micro and macrobiological constituents of a particular growth medium should be considered.

There are often instances of both protected and outside crops where the biological populations must be controlled for continued use of a growth medium or monocropping to be economic. Any method that aims to control or modify the biological properties of a medium must be without persistant effects on its desirable physical, chemical or biological properties, and not leave toxic residues for an unreasonable time. The frequently used term 'soil sterilization' may suffice from the practical viewpoint, but this would imply to the scientist the destruction of the entire biological population of a medium. It has been shown that media may contain beneficial bacteria essential for maintaining nutrient and other cycles. Therefore, since we aim to control only harmful organisms, it is more exact to describe the process as 'partial soil sterilization': this includes the maintenance and restoration of satisfactory conditions, and the eradication of pest and disease organisms.

Partial sterilization by heat

There are three basic methods of partial sterilization suitable for horticulture — *electrical discharge, heat* and *chemicals*, although only the latter two are used commercially.

It is well established that all life in the soil is killed at 127°C. The techniques of heating soil have followed the discovery that the majority of the most harmful organisms are killed by temperatures up to 82°C, whereas many of the desirable bacteria remain unharmed. The temperature at which an organism is killed differs according to the species, its condition and duration of the heat treatment, but for practical purposes the following generalizations may be made.

Some eelworm species (for example *Heterodera marioni*) are killed at 46°C. All weed seeds that have absorbed soil moisture have a relatively low thermal death point of 54°C or below. The macroscopic soil fauna are also killed at this temperature.

Most of the soil-borne pathogens that have had their thermal death points studied are controlled by temperatures below 60°C; these include fungi such as *Rhizoctonia solani, Pythium* spp., *Fusarium roseum f. cerealis* and *Colletotrichum atramentarium*. Tomato mosaic virus has the notably high inactivation temperature of 90°C, and survives even higher temperatures if in thick root tissues.

Traditionally steam has been used as the source of heat when partially sterilizing soils. It has generally been accepted that the cost of steaming prohibits its use outside, but it is still widely practised by growers of protected crops, particularly in glasshouses in many parts of the world. Most glasshouse nurseries have had steam available either direct from their own boiler systems or from mobile steam boilers, which are taken from one nursery to another and hired under a contract for the duration of the treatment.

There are several systems for the application of steam, but basically it is either injected from perforated pipes below the plant beds or on the soil surface under covers, subsequently penetrating downwards from the surface. The steam condenses on the cooler surfaces of the first particles with which it comes into contact, thus raising their temperature. Adjacent particles heat up when the first ones are at the same temperature as the steam. Thus the heat moves forward in a 'front' from the point of introduction.

If steam is passed into a medium faster than it can be condensed, there is a tendency for it to be lost to the atmosphere. In commercial practice it is advisable to ensure that the amount of steam being generated by the boiler per hour is equated with the area to be 'steamed'. This is known in practice as *balanced steaming*. It is vital that the heat front reaches all particles, but the passage of steam into lumps or clods may be impaired, particularly near the surface. Therefore steaming is more efficient when the medium is well broken up or friable.

Steaming from the surface downwards is frequently practised, although the depth of partial sterilization is not likely to be greater than about 150 mm (approximately 6 inches). Therefore, a more thorough technique is the injection of steam into grids, spikes or existing tile drains which have been positioned in the lower profile of plant beds. Steam will also move laterally and downwards to some extent depending on the degree of compaction, isolating materials or water table. The basic design of apparatus for steam injection has evolved very little since the end of the last century when the technique was first introduced. The steam plough, whereby the steam injecting apparatus is slowly winched through the area undergoing treatment is used in some areas, particularly in Scandinavia. Generally, the impediments in glasshouses such as purlins and fixed heating-distribution systems have reduced the potentially efficient use of these implements, but there is increasing interest in steam ploughs in Britain because of improved design of the implement, and partly because of more accessible plant beds in modern glasshouses.

A mobile grid (steam plough) (figure 5.2) has recently been developed at the National Institute of Agricultural Engineering. The apparatus consists of perforated pipes attached to a framework with rollers to control the depth of steam injection. The grid is winched through the soil at a speed of 8 m/h (25 ft/h). This grid is capable of satisfactory partial sterilization to a depth of 0.4–0.45 m (16–18 in.).

The lack of multidiscipline teams researching and developing has probably reduced the potential evolutionary rate of more suitable systems in this area of horticultural technology. However, factors that have aroused interest are an increased knowledge of the importance of

Figure 5.2   Mobile grid (steam plough) developed at the National Institute of Agricultural Engineering. Photograph by courtesy of Burgess and Co. Engineers Limited, Bracknell, Berkshire.

antagonists and the possible problems of toxicity following heat treatment. It was indicated earlier that antagonists could play an important part in suppressing plant pathogens to a relatively low level. There is evidence that when high-temperature regimes are used for partial sterilization, there is an unnecessary reduction in the overall micro-organism population. This can lead to a situation in which pathogens are able to invade a medium, or a small population of surviving pathogens is able quickly to reproduce in the absence of antagonists; this state of affairs is sometimes referred to as a *biological vacuum*.

On some soils, particularly the brick earths used for tomato production by some glasshouse growers in the British Isles, there is a tendency for manganese toxicity to arise following partial sterilization with steam. The occurrence of the toxicity is somewhat unpredictable, but generally it is likely to be similar to steaming where the pH is neutral or below neutral, the available phosphate is low and the medium has been subjected to a high temperature; this applies particularly after prolonged heating. The occurrence of nitrite, nitrate and ammonia toxicities are also more likely to occur following periods of prolonged steaming.

In addition to these detrimental factors of chemical and biological origin, there is the overall economic factor of operational cost. Indeed economic pressures in some areas have accelerated growers' searches for improved methods of partial sterilization. Several workers have advocated the use of lower temperatures and in terms of fuel cost this is to be encouraged. The temperature of steam is normally 100°C, but it has already been noted that plant pathogens are controlled below this temperature. Thus the feasibility of diluting steam with air becomes apparent. This technique has been developed and is known as *steam-air mix* (or aerated steam). The use of steam-air mixes at temperatures of 60°C will normally be satisfactory if maintained for 30 minutes. A notable exception is the control of tobacco mosaic virus. It has been shown that this important virus affecting tomato crops is not always inactivated in crop residues even when temperatures of 100°C have been reached, the aerated steam technique is therefore not entirely satisfactory for most tomato growers.

Chemical sterilization
Chemicals have been used for partial soil sterilization for over a hundred years. Some of the earliest records indicate that at the end of the last century carbon disulphide was applied to soils in French vineyards. More recently the exploitation of chemicals as soil fumigants has been encouraged by rising costs of steam application. The technology of chemical application has evolved and a wide range of materials has been screened. This has led to preparations suitable for the control of specific problems. For example, there are chemicals available as nematocides, which can be used economically in both field and protected cropping, although as yet there are only a few chemicals suitable as soil fumigants for the control of many fungal pathogens. Most chemical sterilants will not eradicate tomato mosaic virus in the root debris in the soil.

In some parts of the world the term *soil fumigation* is preferred to partial soil sterilization by chemicals. The principle of chemical sterilants is the application of a compound referred to as a precursor, which may itself control the pathogen or may be formulated to change on contact with the medium into the active ingredient. Thus

precursor → active ingredient → breakdown product → dispersal product

This pathway may be shortened at either end according to the nature of the chemical applied and the ultimate breakdown products.

The important factors when searching for suitable substances are (1) that the material can be handled safely by workers, (2) that the time for it to disperse or ultimately break down into harmless end products is relatively short, and (3) that the temperature for chemical activity is within the range of temperatures experienced in practice.

Some materials in current use do not necessarily conform to this ideal. *Methyl bromide* is a notable exception; although it disperses very quickly it is extremely hazardous to users and the authorities in most countries only allow licensed contractors to apply it. Conversely *methyl isothiocyanate* is considered safe to apply but takes a longer time to finally clear. The chemical precursors in the form of prills, granules or solutions are normally applied at stations in the medium, although direct application of a gas under polythene sheets is sometimes adopted. Chemical sterilants are applied normally to fallow areas and the time for their application and clearance should be taken into account when planning crops. Commercial producers are sometimes reluctant to terminate previous crops in order to allow sufficient time for the whole operation.

The application rate of the precursor is calculated to provide for a three-dimensional diffusion of the active ingredient in vapour form. Some percolation of the liquid phase may take place when applied as a liquid, but it is generally accepted that the sterilant works as a vapour. The rate of diffusion will ultimately depend on such factors as soil physical conditions (including particle size and moisture content), temperature and molecular weight of the fumigant. Because of vapourization the soil surface is temporarily sealed during treatment, since otherwise the chemical may escape before the treatment has been completed. This seal is adequately achieved with polythene, particularly when using very hazardous materials, but with other materials it may be quite satisfactory to simply seal the surface with water. If the rate of loss by evaporation is high, the water seal may evaporate before the vapours have completed their objective, in which case the re-application of a water seal is indicated. Care must, however, be taken here to avoid risks to workers from remaining gases. There are occasions where neither a polythene nor a water seal are used, but the soil surface at, the injection point is simply compressed immediately after application.

When considering the dispersal of the chemical, the temperature of the medium and its water content during the treatment must be taken into account. Local knowledge is useful here, particularly regarding water tables which may rise to dissolve or trap the active ingredient. The release of this active ingredient is thereby made difficult or even impossible until the medium drains and substrate temperatures increase again in the following growing season. Such problems can lead to disastrous results by chemical action during the production of the following crop. A similar situation exists when the organic or clay particles adsorb the precursor or its subsequent active ingredient. This too may lead to an extension of the optimum duration before complete release of the chemicals. For example, in glasshouses the residues of methyl isothiocyanate following the use of metham-sodium (sodium methyldithiocarbamate) have occasionally been responsible for phytotoxicity of tomato plants.

The best policy for management is to allow time for clearance of the previous crop, application of the chemical, volatilization and finally the release of the residues and end products. This should provide for the unhindered programme for the subsequent crop and applies particularly in temperate regions where there may be high investment and crop value.

Overall effects of partial sterilization
Many research workers have attempted to determine the overall effects of

sterilization, whether by heat or chemicals. The effects of controlling the obvious pathogens can be seen, but research workers have become aware of the dangers of creating a biological vacuum, sometimes referred to as a 'boomerang effect'. This 'vacuum' refers to the rapid recolonization by undesirable pathogens in the absence of beneficial microflora.

Some of the increased crop vigour experienced after a successful partial sterilization programme is attributed to more than the control of known pathogens. The use of heat, particularly in the higher temperature range, can interfere with the bacterial populations responsible for maintaining the nitrogen cycle, and a temporary inhibition of nitrification may take place with subsequent restoration and even greater populations and activity than before.

With some of the chemical sterilants it is likely that a final breakdown to nitrogen products takes place. Some workers have suggested that breakdown products yield carbonic and sulphuric acids which in turn give rise to an increased availability of minerals. It has also been shown that plants can sometimes utilize ammonia more readily than nitrates; in some instances (as with steam applications) the production of ammonia and nitrites is excessive, giving rise to toxicity. It is therefore important not to add liming materials or bulky organics until after steaming. However, as such post-sterilization addition of bulky organic material may introduce pathogens, the practice should be carefully considered before it is used. It is now generally accepted that low concentrations of some sterilants, for example the chlorinated hydrocarbons, such as D–D (a mixture of dichloropropene and dichloropropane), stimulate microbial activity, which in turn increases the activity of crop plants. It is important that horticulturists be made aware of the practical implications of applying these techniques. A full evaluation of each situation should help the decision as to which technique and materials to use. After this it is important to provide ideal conditions so that the partial sterilization produces maximum benefit and, finally, possible after-effects should be considered in relation to cropping programmes, and nutrient regimes modified accordingly.

SUMMARY

Good management of soils and growth media is essential for efficient crop production, and attention should be paid to the adverse effects of mechanization. When soil is compacted aeration, drainage and root growth are restricted. Compaction can have several causes, such as using a tractor when the soil is too wet, formation of a 'pan' after successive ploughings at the same depth, or it can result from large rain or irrigation water droplets falling on the soil surface.

Modern methods of crop production in a weed free environment and mulching have greatly reduced the need for cultivations and allow good soil physical conditions to be maintained.

Plant nutrients are normally classified as macronutrients (carbon, hydrogen, oxygen, nitrogen, sulphur, phosphorus, calcium, magnesium and potassium) used in large quantities by the plants, or micronutrients (boron, iron, zinc, copper, chlorine and molybdenum) which, although usually essential, are required in small amounts. Appropriate fertilizers should be added to soils and growth media according to the particular crop's requirements and soil reserves as determined by analysis. Liquid feeding via the medium or the foliage are becoming increasingly important techniques, particularly in the glasshouse industry.

Organic materials can help to maintain the soil's physical properties as well as supplying nutrients. Farmyard manure and other bulky organic materials (such as straw, processed crop residues, poultry manure and sewage sludge) are widely used for this purpose according to their local availability. The value of these materials should always be assessed on cost, nutrient content and soil physical amelioration grounds.

The maintenance of biological properties of the soil is increasingly important with the adoption of monocropping systems, which lead to the build-up of specific pathogens or pests. Heat or chemical fumigants are used for partial soil sterilization according to the range of pathogens present.

BIBLIOGRAPHY

GENERAL

Comprehensive reviews

(1) BLACK, C. A. (1968), *Soil—plant relationships, 2nd edn.*, Wiley.
This book gives over 1300 references.

(2) RUSSELL, E. W. (1973), *Soil conditions and plant growth, 10th edn.*, Longmans. pp. 849.

Techniques of soil analysis

(3) BLACK, C. A. (Editor-in-Chief) (1965), *Methods of soil analysis,* American Society of Agronomy Inc., Madison, Wisconsin.
In two volumes, this book covers mineralogical, chemical and microbiological aspects.

(4) HESSE, P. R. (1971), *A textbook of soil chemical analysis,* Murray, London.
Methods with explanations of background theory can be found in this book.

CHAPTER 1 MICROSTRUCTURE OF SOIL MATERIALS

Clay mineral structures

(1) MARSHALL, C. E. (1964), *The physical chemistry and mineralogy of soils: Vol. 1 Soil materials,* Wiley.

Ion exchange

(2) KELLEY, W. P. (1948), *Cation exchange in soils,* Am. Chem. Soc. Monograph No. 109, Reinhold.
Unfortunately now somewhat dated.

(3) BOLT, G. H. (1967), Cation exchange equations used in soil science. *Neth. J. agric. Sci.,* **15**, 81—103.
An excellent review.

Colloidal properties

(4) VAN OLPHEN, H. (1963), *Introduction to clay colloid chemistry.* Wiley.
A very clear exposition of the colloidal properties of clays.

Adsorbed water on clays

(5) LOW, P. F. (1961), Physical chemistry of clay—water interaction, *Adv. Agron.,* **13**, 269.
The long-range order hypothesis.

Non-crystalline inorganic soil constituents

(6) MITCHELL, B. N., FARMER V. C., and McHARDY, W. J. (1964). Amorphous inorganic materials in soils, *Adv. Agron.,* **16**, 327.

Soil organic matter

(7) STEELINK, C. (1963), What is humic acid? *J. chem. Educ.*, **40**, 379.

(8) FELBECK, G. T. Jr. (1965), Structural chemistry of humic substances. *Adv. Agron.*, **17**, 327.

Clay organic complexes

(9) GREENLAND, D. J. (1965), Interaction between clays and organic compounds in soils, *Soils Fertil.*, **28**, 415 and 521.

(10) MORTLAND, M. M. (1970), Clay-organic complexes and interactions, *Adv. Agron.*, **22**, 75.

(11) SCHNITZER, M. and KODAMA, H. (1966), Adsorption of a soil humic compound by montmorillonite. *Science, N.Y.*, **153**, 70.
     Fulvic acid—montmorillonite interlamellar complexes prepared in the laboratory.

CHAPTER 2   THE MOLECULAR ENVIRONMENT OF PLANT ROOTS

(1) HILLEL, D. (1971), *Soil and water: Physical principles and processes*, Academic Press.
     A very lucid account.

(2) CHILDS, E. C. (1969), *An introduction to the physical basis of soil water phenomena*, Wiley.
     A more advanced text.

(3) KOHNKE, H. (1968), *Soil physics*, McGraw-Hill.
     An introductory treatment.

(4) BAVER, L. D., GARDNER, W. H. and GARDNER, W. R. (1972), *Soil physics*, 4th ed., Wiley.

(5) GRABLE, A. R. (1966), Soil aeration and plant growth. *Adv. Agron.*, **18**, 56.

CHAPTER 3   THE IONIC ENVIRONMENT OF PLANT ROOTS

General

(1) FRIED, M. and BROESHART, H. (1967), *The soil—plant system in relation to inorganic nutrition*, Academic Press.
     A comprehensive review including plant aspects.

Potentiometric C.E.C. measurement

(2) BROWN, I. C. (1943), A rapid method of determining exchangeable hydrogen and total exchangeable bases of soils. *Soil Sci.*, **56**, 353.

Potassium fixation

(3) AGARVAL, R. R. (1960), Potassium fixation in soils. *Soils Fertil.*, **23**, 375.

(4) SCHUFFELEN, A. C., and VAN DER MAREL, H. W. (1954), Potassium fixation in soils. *Potass. symp.*, 169.
     Review papers.

Soil acidity
(5)   JENNY, H. (1961), Reflections on the soil acidity merry-go-round. *Proc. Soil Sci. Soc. Am.*, **25**, 428.
A lively review of the theories on the nature of soil acidity.

Salinity
(6)   US SALINITY LABORATORY STAFF (1954), *Diagnosis and improvement of saline and alkali soils*, USDA Handbook 60.

Soil phosphate
(7)   LARSEN, S. (1967), Soil phosphorus. *Adv. Agron.*, **19**, 151.
General review by the originator of the '*L* value' technique.

(8)   CHANG, S. C., and JACKSON, M. L. (1957), Fractionation of soil phosphorus. *Soil Sci.*, **84**, 133.
The chemical fractionation procedure.

Ion movement in soils
(9)   OLSEN, S. R., and KEMPER, W. D. (1969), Movement of nutrients to plant roots. *Adv. Agron.*, **20**, 91.

Potassium potential
(10) WOODRUFF, C. M. (1955), Ionic equilibria between clay and dilute salt solutions. *Proc. Soil Sci. Soc. Am.*, **19**, 36.

Limiting-ion ratios
(11) BECKETT, P. (1972), Critical cation activity ratios. *Adv. Agron.*, **24**, 379.

Phosphate potential
(12) SCHOFIELD, R. K. (1955), Can a precise meaning be given to 'available' soil phosphorus? *Soils Fertil.*, **18**, 373.
The phosphate potential concept.

(13) WILD, A. (1964), Soluble phosphate in soil and uptake by plants. *Nature, Lond.*, **203**, 326.
Phosphate potential and plant uptake of phosphate.

CHAPTER 4   MACROSCOPIC STRUCTURE AND PROPERTIES OF GROWTH MEDIA

General
(1)   COOKE, G. W. (1967), *The control of soil fertility*, Crosby Lockwood, London.

(2)   Ministry of Agriculture Fisheries and Food (1970), *Modern farming and the soil:* Report of the Agriculture Advisory Council on soil structure and fertility. H.M.S.O., London.

CHAPTER 5   THE MANAGEMENT OF SOILS FOR HORTICULTURAL CROPS

General
(1)   WHITTINGTON, W. J. (1969), *Root Growth*, Butterworths, London.

Nutrition

(2) HEMINGWAY, R. G. (1961), The mineral composition of farmyard manure, *Emp. J. exp. Agric.*, **29**, 14.

(3) COOKE, G. W. (1972), *Fertilizing for maximum yield*, Crosby Lockwood, London.

(4) SAUCHELLI, V. (1969), *Trace elements in agriculture*, Van Nostrand Reinhold, New York.

Soil biology

(5) JACKSON, R. M., and RAW, F. (1966), *Life in the soil*, Arnold, London.

(6) GRAY, T. R. G., and WILLIAMS, S. T. (1971), *Soil Micro-organisms*, Oliver and Boyd, Edinburgh.

Partial sterilization

(7) LAWRENCE, W. J. C. (1956), *Soil sterilization*, Allen and Unwin, London.

(8) SAVORY, B. M. (1966), *Specific replant diseases*, Commonwealth Agriculture Bureau, East Malling.

Container media

(9) BAKER, K. F. (1957), *The U.C. system for producing healthy container-grown plants*, University of California college of Agriculture.

(10) Ministry of Agriculture Fisheries and Food (1970), *Straw substrates for the production of crops in greenhouses*, Short Term Leaflet 105, H.M.S.O., London.

GLOSSARY

Activity   For substances in solution, activity is a measure of the effective solute concentration. The activity and the concentration of a solute are identical only in very dilute solutions but not otherwise.

Amorphous materials   The *microstructure* of such materials shows no regularity when examined with appropriate techniques.

Artificial growth media   Porous media providing plants with nutrients and with anchorage like natural soils, but prepared artificially rather than naturally formed.

Calcicole   A plant that thrives on a calcareous soil.

Calcifuge   A plant that thrives on an acid soil.

Chemisorption   Adsorption usually involving *primary valence bonds* and therefore stronger and more specific than physical adsorption.

Coagulation   The process of aggregation of particles in a dispersion brought about by electrical double-layer compression due to the presence of simple electrolytes.

Complex ions   Ions formed by the attachment of other ions or molecules to an ion to form a stable, charged entity.

Conjugated double bonds   A series of double and single bonds arranged alternately in a molecule, for instance $= CH - CH = CH - CH =$.

Coordination number   The number of nearest neighbours of a given atom in a crystal.

Counterions   Ions at or near a charged surface bearing a charge opposite in sign to that of the surface.

Covalent bond   Chemical bond between two atoms sharing a pair of electrons. The shared electron pair is equivalent to one covalent bond.

Crystalline materials Materials with a regular microstructure. Full crystallinity implies regularity in three dimensions; clay minerals are usually of limited, two-dimensional crystallinity.

Density of surface charge The number of electric charges on a unit surface area. Used in this book mainly to characterize clay minerals.

Dielectric constant A property of a substance determining the magnitude of the force acting between two electric charges placed in the substance unit distance apart. The force is inversely proportional to the dielectric constant.

Differential thermal analysis A thermal method for characterizing materials. The heat effects (both endothermic and exothermic), following chemical and physical changes in a substance brought about by heating the substance at a known rate are recorded.

Equimolar ion exchange Ion exchange in which the mole ratio of the exchanged ions is apparently unity.

Equivalent ion exchange Regular ion exchange in which the ratio of equivalents of ions exchanged is unity.

Equivalent spherical diameter An experimentally accessible characteristic of small particles of irregular shape; the radius of a spherical particle that would sediment with the same velocity as the non-spherical particle actually observed. Used to define particle size fractions in soil suspensions.

Erosion The removal of the top layers of natural soils by wind or by surface runoff.

Evapotranspiration The combined processes of evaporation of water from a soil plus the transpiration through plants growing on it.

Flocculation Process of aggregation in dispersions brought about by bridging of particles by polymers of high molecular weight.

Glasshouse Any structure used for the production of protected crops clad with glass or other light-transmitting material.

Homoionic clay mineral A mineral in which all the negatively charged sites are neutralized by a single type of exchangeable cation.

Hydration *Solvation* of molecules or of ions with water as the solvent.

Hydrogen bond A relatively weak bond between a hydrogen atom attached covalently to an electronegative atom (commonly nitrogen or oxygen) and another electronegative atom; for instance, $O - H \ldots N$.

Hysteresis The phenomenon of dependence of the state of a system on its previous history.

Infrared spectroscopy A useful technique for characterizing substances by recording the absorption of radiation in the infrared region of the electromagnetic spectrum by the substance.

Interacting electrical double layers On close approach, the diffuse parts of the electrical double layers on two charged particles in suspension overlap giving rise to electrical double-layer interaction.

Ionic bond Chemical bond between two atoms involving the transfer of one or more electrons. Each transferred electron is equivalent to one ionic bond.

Matric potential or *matric suction* A component of the total soil water potential associated with the presence of the soil solid phase or soil matric.

Mean hydrodynamic pore radius A characteristic of the pore space of porous media, proportional to the pore volume/surface area ratio in a given amount of the medium.

Microstructure Structure on an atomic scale. Applied in this book to soil materials.

Mineralization Broad term to cover the processes of conversion of organic soil nitrogen into ammonium, mediated by a wide range of nonspecific micro-organisms.

Natural soils The thin top layer of the earth's crust supporting vegetation, formed largely as a result of natural (geological, climatic, chemical and biological) processes.

Nitrification Broad term covering the processes involved in the oxidation of ammonium to nitrate in soils, mediated by specific nitrifying bacteria.

Non-interacting electrical double layers Electrical double layers formed spontaneously at the surfaces of charged particles in solution, in the absence of overlapping double layers in the immediate vicinity.

Nuclear magnetic resonance   An electromagnetic technique for characterizing the electronic environment in which certain atoms (commonly hydrogen) in a molecule are situated.

Occluded phosphate   Phosphate in soils occurring in isolated 'pockets' wholly enclosed inside grains of other minerals such as ferric oxide.

Primary valence bonds   Strong chemical bonds of the covalent or ionic type.

Rhizosphere   The volume of a soil or other growth medium in close proximity to the plant root surface.

Solute potential or *solute suction*   A component of the total soil water potential associated with the presence of freely diffusible solutes in the soil solution.

Solvation   The attachment of molecules of the solvent to molecules or ions of a solute. In a broader sense, attachment of molecules of a second solute to molecules or ions of another type in the same solution is also referred to as solvation.

Specific conductance   The measured conductance of a solution corrected for the dimensions of the cell used for the conductivity measurement.

Steric   Relating to the spatial arrangement of atoms in a molecule.

Thermodynamic ion-exchange constant   The true ion-exchange constant analogous to the selectivity coefficient, but derived from the *activities* of the ions adsorbed and in solution, rather than from their concentrations.

Total potential energy of interaction   Characteristic of the interaction (repulsion and attraction) between two charged particles; in this book, clay crystallites in suspension. It can be derived from the forces of interaction between the particles by integrating the force over the distance of particle separation.

van der Waals forces   Universal intermolecular forces of an electrical nature between all types of polar and/or nonpolar molecules.

Whole soils   Unfractionated natural soils.

CGS AND SI UNITS

Alongside the old established CGS system of units, the Système International d'Unités or SI is now increasingly used in scientific work. The essential difference between the two systems is that the CGS system regards the centimetre(cm), the gram(g) and the second(sec) as primary units, while SI is based on the metre(m), the kilogramme(kg) and the second(s). The table below lists some useful conversion factors by which CGS units have to be multiplied to obtain the corresponding SI units.

Quantity	CGS unit	SI unit	To convert CGS unit to SI unit, multiply by
Length	centimetre (cm)	metre (m)	10^{-2}
Volume	litre (l)	metre^3	10^{-3}
Mass	gram (g)	kilogramme (kg)	10^{-3}
Time	second (sec)	second (s)	1
Force or weight	dyne ($=$g cm sec^{-2})	newton (N) ($=$ m kg s^{-2})	10^{-5}
	gram weight ($= 981$ dyne)		
Pressure	dyne cm^{-2}	pascal (Pa) ($=$ N m^{-2})	10^{-1}
	mm Hg at $0°$C $= 1333$ dyne cm^{-2})		133
	atmosphere ($= 760$ mm Hg at $0°$C)		1.01×10^5
Energy or work	erg ($=$ dyne cm)	joule (J)	10^{-7}
	calorie (thermochemical)		4.184
	litre atmosphere		101.3

INDEX